Table of Contents

Mathematical Practices Handbook . . . . SMPi

Standards in boldface are the focus standards that address major lesson content.

Table of Contents continued

Standards in boldface are the focus standards that address major lesson content.

Updated for 2017

Vice President of Product Development: Adam Berkin
Editorial Director: Cindy Tripp
Director, Customization and Correlations: Abigail Jungreis
Project Managers: Deb Golumbek, Sherry Pilkerton
Executive Editor: Penny Dowdy
Editor: Ruth Estabrook
Cover Design and Illustrator: Matt Pollock
Book Design: Jeremy Spiegel

ISBN 978-1-4957-3588-2
©2017–Curriculum Associates, LLC
North Billerica, MA 01862

Standards in boldface are the focus standards that address major lesson content.

MATHEMATICAL PRACTICES HANDBOOK

We use our math thinking to figure out all kinds of problems, even hard problems from real life.

There are eight math habits that will help make your math thinking grow stronger.

Keep practicing! You'll be learning to think like a math pro. Then you'll be ready to take on any problem.

THE 8 MATH HABITS

1 Solve problems.
Keep looking for clues until you solve the problem.

2 Think and reason.
Make sense of the words and the numbers in a problem.

3 Show and explain.
Share your math ideas to help others understand you.

4 Use math in the real world.
Solve problems in real life.

5 Choose a tool.
Decide when to use tools like a diagram, a ruler, or mental math.

6 Be clear and precise.
Try to be exactly right in what you say and do.

7 Zoom in and zoom out.
Look for what's the same and what's different.

8 Use patterns.
Look for patterns in math to find shortcuts.

Read more about each math habit on the pages that follow.

MATH HABIT ❶

Solve problems.

Keep looking for clues until you solve the problem.

For some math problems, you may not know where to start. Try different ways to find a solution and look for clues about which way works best. Then check that your answer makes sense.

To solve problems

Ask Yourself

- Can I say what the problem is asking for?
- Can I ask questions to understand it better?
- Can I think about what does or doesn't make sense?
- Can I try a different way if I need to?

Then, Discuss with a Partner

- I thought the problem didn't make sense until I asked …
- I know my answer makes sense because …

MATH HABIT ②

SMP 2 Reason abstractly and quantitatively.

Think and reason.

Make sense of the words and the numbers in a problem.

Reasoning is a way of thinking that puts ideas together. If you know one thing, then you know another thing. Reasoning is using math rules and common sense together.

To use reasoning to solve a problem

Ask Yourself

- Can I show how whole numbers and decimals are related?

- When I see an equation, can I think of a situation that would go with it?

- When I read a problem, can I write an equation to find the answer?

- Can I try out my answer to see if it makes sense in the problem?

Then, Discuss with a Partner

- I turned the problem into numbers when I wrote …

- I think my answer makes sense because …

MATH HABIT ❸

Show and explain.

Share your math ideas to help others understand you.

When you explain your math ideas to others, it helps you understand them even better. And that helps you solve other problems later. When you listen to other people, you get new ideas too.

To help explain your ideas or listen to others

Ask Yourself

- Can I use words to show how to solve the problem?
- Can I use pictures or act out the problem with objects?
- Can I ask questions to understand another person's ideas better?

Then, Discuss with a Partner

- I showed my ideas when I wrote ...
- I explained my ideas when I said ...

MATH HABIT ④

SMP 4 Model with mathematics.

Use math in the real world.

Solve problems in real life.

One of the best ways to use your math thinking is to solve real problems. Words tell the story for the problem. Math can turn the words into a model, such as a picture or an equation.

You can use models to solve problems about shopping, art projects, sports, cooking, or … almost anything!

To solve a real-life problem

Ask Yourself

- Can I draw a picture, write an equation, or use a different model to show the math?
- Can I use my math model to solve the problem?
- Can I check that my answer makes sense?

Then, Discuss with a Partner

- I used a math model to show the problem when I …
- I know my answer makes sense because …

MATH HABIT ⑤

SMP 5 Use appropriate tools strategically.

Choose a tool.

Decide when to use tools like a diagram, a ruler, or mental math.

There are many tools to use in math. You can use a pencil to do a lot of math. Sometimes you need a ruler, or maybe a diagram. Often you can just do the math in your head.

To choose the best tools

Ask Yourself
- Can I do some problems in my head?
- Can I write the problem on paper?
- Can I make a table or a diagram?
- Can I use a ruler to solve the problem?

Then, Discuss with a Partner
- The tools I chose for this problem are ...
- I chose these tools because ...

MATH HABIT ⑥

SMP 6 Attend to precision.

Be clear and precise.

Try to be exactly right in what you say and do.

Everybody likes to be right when they do math. But sometimes people make mistakes. So it's good to check your work. And it's good to say exactly what you mean when you talk about your math ideas.

To be exactly right

Ask Yourself

- Can I use words that will help everyone understand my math ideas?
- Can I ask questions to understand the meaning of math words I don't know?
- Can I find different ways to check my work when I multiply or add?
- Can I always think about whether my answer makes sense?

Then, Discuss with a Partner

- I was careful to use the right words when I …
- I checked my answer by …

MATH HABIT ⑦

Zoom in and zoom out.

Look for what's the same and what's different.

Math follows rules. Think about these equations:

$3 \times 1 = 3$

$4 \times 1 = 4$

You can *zoom out* to look at what's the *same* about problems. They show that any number times 1 is that number.

You can also *zoom in* to see what's *different* about problems. The number multiplied by 1 is different in each problem.

To zoom in and zoom out

Ask Yourself

- Can I see how decimals and fractions are both similar and different?
- Can I see how decimals and whole numbers are both similar and different?
- Can I see how shapes are different but are made from other shapes that are the same?

Then, Discuss with a Partner

- I zoomed out and used a math rule when I …
- I zoomed in and found a difference when I looked at …

MATH HABIT ⑧

SMP 8 Look for and express regularity in repeated reasoning.

Use patterns.

Look for patterns in math to find shortcuts.

It's important in math to pay close attention. You might find a pattern or see a math idea.

Think about the pattern you see when you count by elevens:

11, 22, 33, 44, 55 …

You can use the pattern to make a good guess about what comes next.

To use patterns

Ask Yourself

- Can I find a pattern in a math problem?
- Can I use clear math words to describe my pattern?
- Can I make a good guess about what is next?

Then, Discuss with a Partner

- I saw a pattern in this problem when I looked at …
- I made a good guess about the pattern when I …

Unit 1
The Number System

Real-World Connection You will encounter positive and negative numbers in many situations in your life. Money will be deposited and withdrawn from your bank account. The stock you have in your favorite ice cream brand may increase by $\frac{1}{8}$ one day and go down by $\frac{1}{2}$ the next day. Niagara Falls currently erodes at a rate of about 1 foot each year. It is hoped that erosion will fall to 1 foot every 10 years. Will the attraction look the same by the time you are 50 years old?

In This Unit You will solve problems with positive and negative integers using the four operations. You will also learn how to describe rational numbers as terminating or repeating decimals. You will add, subtract, multiply, and divide with rational numbers.

✔ Self Check

Before starting this unit, check off the skills you know below. As you complete each lesson, see how many more you can check off!

I can:	Before this unit	After this unit
add and subtract positive and negative integers, for example: $-3 + (-4) = -7$	☐	☐
multiply and divide positive and negative integers, for example: $-2 \cdot (-4) = 8$	☐	☐
add and subtract rational numbers, for example: $-2.5 + 3.8 = 1.3$	☐	☐
multiply and divide rational numbers, for example: $-\frac{1}{4} \div \frac{1}{3} = -\frac{3}{4}$	☐	☐
solve word problems with rational numbers	☐	☐

💭 Think It Through

When do you add positive and negative integers?

You can use positive and negative integers to represent quantities you see in sports, games, business, science, and in other areas of your life.

For instance, in a game, you might gain 5 points if you answer the question correctly and lose 5 points if you answer the question incorrectly. The numbers 5 and −5 are on opposite sides of the number line and have the same distance from 0 on the number line. This means that the numbers have the same **absolute value**.

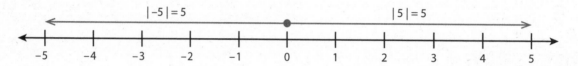

Think What happens when you add an integer to its opposite?

You can use a number line to picture what happens when you add an integer to its opposite.

Look at the number line above. The distance from 0 to −5 is represented by an arrow pointing to the left. The distance from 0 to 5 is represented by an arrow pointing to the right. Because $|5| = |-5|$, you know the distances and arrows are equal in length.

The sum of 5 and −5 is shown on the number line below. If you move 5 units in the positive direction and then move 5 units in the negative direction, you will be back at 0.

> ✏️ **Circle** the arrow that represents −5 on the number line.

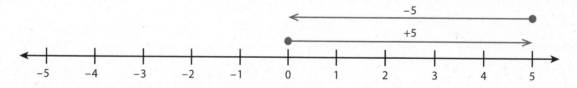

Two numbers that have a sum of zero are **additive inverses**. In this case, −5 is the additive inverse of 5 because $5 + (-5) = 0$. For the same reason, 5 is the additive inverse of −5.

Think How do you model integer addition on a number line?

When adding or subtracting a negative number, you write the negative number in parentheses to separate it from the operation symbol.

Correct	Incorrect
3 + (−5)	3 + −5
4 − (−3)	4 − −3

The number line below represents −2 + (−4). You start at −2 and **move left 4 units**, ending at −6. The sum −2 + (−4) is −6. When adding two negative numbers, you start on the left side of 0 and always move left, so the answer is always negative.

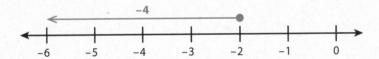

The number line below represents 7 + (−5). You start at 7 and **move left 5 units** to add −5. You end at 2, so 7 + (−5) = 2.

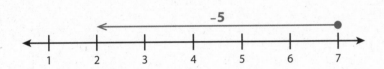

Will the sum of −8 and +3 be positive or negative? Explain.

You can use this same process to add 5 + (−7). You start at 5 and **move left 7 units**. You end at −2, so 5 + (−7) = −2.

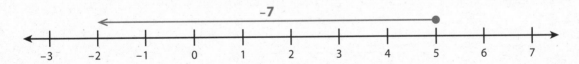

▶ Reflect

1 How is adding integers similar to adding whole numbers? How is it different?

_____

_____

_____

_____

Think About ▶ **Adding Positive and Negative Integers**

🔍 **Let's Explore the Idea** You can use additive inverses to help you understand how to add integers.

2 A fisherman positions his net to −8 feet relative to the surface of the water. How far does he need to raise the net to bring it to the surface of the water? _____

3 A bird 7 feet in the air flies down to the ground. What integer would you use to represent the change in the bird's position? _____

Using a number line helps you to visualize what is happening when adding integers.

4 Use the number line below to show 6 + (−6). The sum 6 + (−6) = _____.

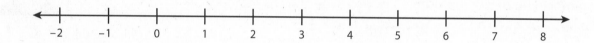

5 Use the number line below to show 11 + (−8). The sum 11 + (−8) = _____.

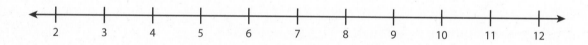

6 Use the number line below to show −4 + (−7). The sum −4 + (−7) = _____.

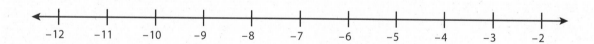

7 Use the number line below to show −4 + 7. The sum −4 + 7 = _____.

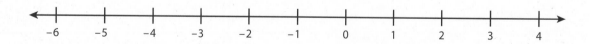

8 Jason's football team lost 6 yards from their starting position and then lost another 5 yards. What number represents a loss of 6 yards? a loss of 5 yards? _____

9 Use a number line to find the team's total loss.

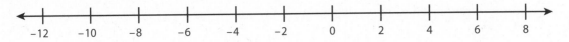

10 On the next play, the team gains 12 yards. Will the team be at their original starting position? Explain.

_____

_____

11 A weather forecaster says the temperature will be about −5°C "give or take" 10 degrees.

What is the greatest possible temperature? _____

What is the least possible temperature? _____

12 Explain how you found your answers to problem 11. _____

_____

_____

Try It Another Way You can add integers by decomposing numbers to form additive inverses that add to 0. For example, to add −8 + 10, you can think of 10 as 8 + 2.

$$-8 + 10 = -8 + (8 + 2)$$
$$= (-8 + 8) + 2$$
$$= 0 + 2$$
$$= 2$$

Use the method shown above to do the problems below. Show your steps.

13 10 + (−4) _____

14 −12 + 7 _____

Connect ▶ **Adding Positive and Negative Integers**

Talk through these problems as a class and write your answers below.

15 **Compare** Show $7 + (-3)$ on the number line below.

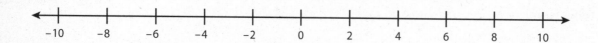

Show $-3 + 7$ on the number line below.

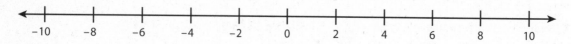

What do you notice about the results? _____

Explain why your number lines end on the same number. _____

_____

16 **Explain** Chase drew the number line below to show $-4 + (-3)$. Is his model accurate? If not, tell what is wrong with his model.

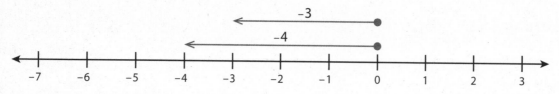

_____

_____

17 **Analyze** On the number line below, the numbers x and y are the same distance from 0. What is $x + y$? Explain how you found your answer.

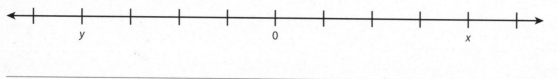

_____

_____

_____

_____

6 **Lesson 1** *Understand* Addition of Positive and Negative Integers

Apply ▶ **Adding Positive and Negative Integers**

18 **Put It Together** Use what you have learned in this lesson to complete this task.

> Mari is participating in National Lemonade Stand Day. She spends $18 for start-up costs, which include supplies to make the lemonade, cups, and advertising.

Part A Describe in detail how Mari could end up with the lemonade stand breaking even. ("Breaking even" means "a profit of 0," or that she makes enough money to pay for her start-up costs but has no money left over.) Your description must include:

- the cost of each type of supply (lemonade, cups, and advertising), with each cost represented as a negative number and in dollars
- the price Mari charges for 1 cup of lemonade, in dollars
- the total amount of sales, in dollars
- the money she has left over after covering her start-up costs, in dollars
- a mathematical expression and model that use the concepts in this lesson to show the amount of profit

_____

_____

_____

_____

Part B Repeat Part A for the situation where Mari's lemonade stand makes a profit (meaning she has enough money to pay for her startup costs and has some money left over). Draw your number line on a separate sheet of paper.

_____

_____

_____

_____

💭 Think It Through

What happens when you subtract positive and negative numbers?

In the previous lesson you represented a problem like $5 + (-3)$ on a number line. You started at 5 and **moved left (in the negative direction) 3** units to represent adding -3. You ended at 2.

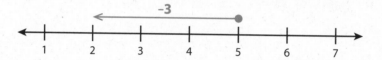

Now let's look at another way to think about this problem.

Think How is subtracting integers like adding integers?

Think about this subtraction problem: $5 - 3 = \boxed{}$.

Because addition and subtraction are inverse operations, you can rewrite this equation as an addition equation.

$3 + \boxed{} = 5$

> What number do I add to 3 to get 5?

You can also use a number line to represent this equation.

Start at 5 and **move left 3**.

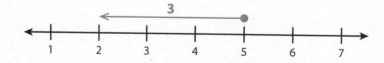

> 🖊 **Circle** the answers on the number line showing $5 + (-3)$ and the number line showing $5 - 3$.

When you look at the number line at the top of the page that represents $5 + (-3)$ and the number line above that represents $5 - 3$, you should notice that they are exactly the same. So, $5 - 3 = 5 + (-3)$.

These two number lines show an important relationship between addition and subtraction. Any subtraction problem can be written as an addition problem.

Think How do you write a subtraction problem as an addition problem?

Look at the two equivalent expressions on the previous page.

5	−	3
5	+	(−3)

What operation is the opposite of subtraction? What is the opposite of a number, *n*?

The first number stays the same.	Use the opposite operation.	Use the opposite of the second number.

This means that every subtraction problem can be written as an addition problem.

So, if you know how to add positive and negative numbers, you know how to subtract them. Here are some other examples:

$4 - 4 = 0$

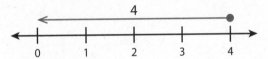

$4 + (-4) = 0$

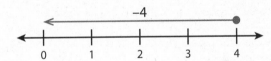

$1 - 3 = -2$

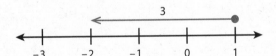

$1 + (-3) = -2$

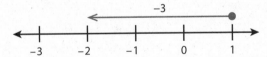

▶ Reflect

1 Why can you write a subtraction problem as an addition problem? How do you write a subtraction problem as an addition problem?

_____

_____

_____

_____

Lesson 2 *Understand* Subtraction of Positive and Negative Integers

Think About ▶ **Subtracting Positive and Negative Integers**

🔍 **Let's Explore the Idea** You can write a subtraction problem as an addition problem.

In problems 2–5, write a subtraction problem to represent the situation. Then write the subtraction problem as an addition problem. Model the addition problem on a number line, and use the number line to answer the question.

2 Adam buys 9 gift cards and gives 6 away. How many does he have left?

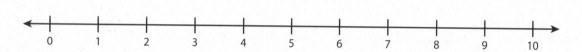

3 Renee is playing a game online. If she gets a total of 25 points, she will have a new high score. She currently has −5 points. What is the difference between a high score of 25 points and the number of points she currently has?

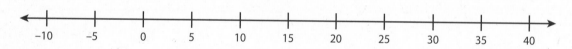

4 Rob is trying to read for 30 minutes each Saturday. He only read for 20 minutes last Saturday. He represents the amount of time he was short of the total 30 minutes as −10 minutes. This Saturday, he wants to make up the difference between the number of minutes he usually reads on Saturday and the number of minutes he was short last Saturday. How many minutes will Rob need to read this Saturday?

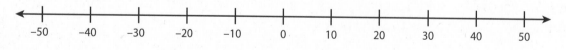

5 The temperature at noon is −4°F. The temperature at 6:00 PM is −12°F. What is the difference between the noon and the 6:00 PM temperatures?

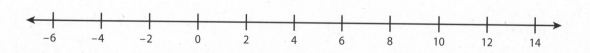

Let's Talk About It
Solve the problems below as a group.

6 Fran rewrites a subtraction problem as an addition problem. The addition problem she writes is $-3 + (-4)$. How could you use a number line to help you write $-3 + (-4)$ as a subtraction problem? _____

_____

7 Look back at problem 6. What was Fran's original subtraction problem? Explain how you got your answer. _____

_____

_____

Use the number line below for problems 8–10.

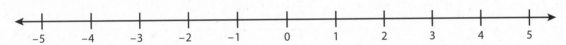

8 What is the distance between 2 and 3 on the number line? _____

What is $|\,3 - 2\,|$? _____ What is the distance between -3 and -2? _____

What is $|\,-3 - (-2)\,|$? _____

9 What is the distance between 4 and 1 on the number line? _____

What is $|\,4 - 1\,|$? _____ What is the distance between -4 and -1? _____

What is $|\,-4 - (-1)\,|$? _____

10 Look at your answers to problems 8 and 9. What do you notice about the absolute value of the difference between two numbers? _____

_____

▶ Try It Another Way Work with your group to solve this problem.

11 Write an absolute value expression to represent the distance between -2 and 4 on a number line. Then evaluate the expression.

_____

Lesson 2 *Understand* Subtraction of Positive and Negative Integers

Connect ▶ **Subtracting Positive and Negative Integers**

Talk through these problems as a class and write your answers below.

12 Compare How are the expressions $8 - 15$ and $8 + (-15)$ alike? How are they different?

_____

_____

_____

_____

_____

13 Explain Describe why you can change a subtraction problem into an addition problem and how to do it. Include an example in your answer and graph each problem on the number lines below. _____

_____

_____

_____

_____

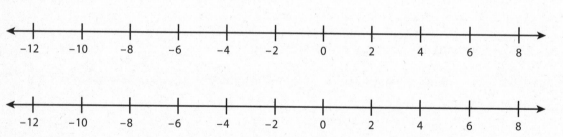

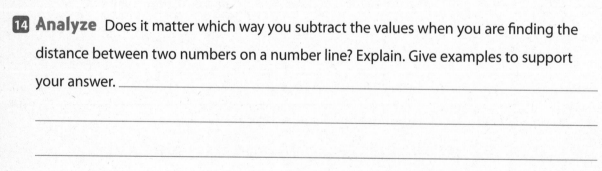

14 Analyze Does it matter which way you subtract the values when you are finding the distance between two numbers on a number line? Explain. Give examples to support your answer. _____

_____

_____

_____

Apply ▶ **Subtracting Positive and Negative Integers**

15 Put It Together Use what you have learned to answer the questions below.

The map of Jean's neighborhood shows the location of Jean's house, her school, her friend Pam's house, and her favorite restaurant.

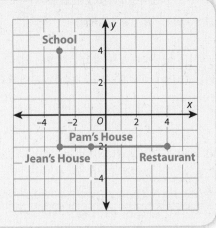

Part A Find each distance described below by finding the absolute value of the difference between the x-coordinates of the two points on the map. Write a subtraction problem and a related addition problem for each distance. Then evaluate your expressions to find the distance.

Restaurant to Pam's House

Subtraction problem _____

Addition problem _____

Distance _____

Pam's House to Jean's House

Subtraction problem _____

Addition problem _____

Distance _____

Part B Refer to the map above. What coordinates do you subtract to find the distance from Jean's house to her school? Explain your reasoning. _____

_____

Part C Write a subtraction problem and a related addition problem for the distance described below. Then evaluate your expressions to find the distance.

Jean's house to school

Subtraction problem _____

Addition problem _____

Distance _____

Lesson 2 *Understand* Subtraction of Positive and Negative Integers **13**

↻ Use What You Know

In previous lessons, you learned about positive and negative numbers. In this lesson, you will learn how to add and subtract positive and negative numbers. Take a look at this problem.

> Amy, Ray, Kim, and Jamal are on a trivia team. They gain points for correct answers and lose points for incorrect answers. During the contest, Amy gains 3 points, Ray loses 4 points, Kim loses 2 points, and Jamal gains 5 points. How many points does the team have at the end of the contest?

Use the math you already know to solve the problem.

a. Which team members can use a positive number to represent their point total?

_____

b. Which team members can use a negative number to represent their point total?

_____

c. Write a positive or negative number to represent the number of points earned by each team member.

Amy's points: _____   Kim's points: _____

Ray's points: _____   Jamal's points: _____

d. What is the number of points Amy and Jamal gain altogether? Would you represent this amount as a positive or negative number? Why?

_____

e. What is the number of points Ray and Kim lose altogether? Would you represent this amount as a positive or negative number? Why?

_____

f. Explain how you could find the total number of points the team has altogether.

_____

In the problem on the previous page, **positive** numbers represent **gains**, and **negative** numbers represent **losses**. You can use a number line to add positive and negative numbers. **Move right to add** a positive number, and **move left to add** a negative number.

Amy has 3 points, so start at 3 on the number line.

Ray **lost 4** points. $3 - 4$ means $3 + (-4)$. From 3, **move left 4** to add -4 points. The result is -1.

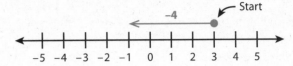

Kim **lost 2** points. $-1 - 2$ means $-1 + (-2)$. From -1, **move left 2** to add -2 points. The result is -3.

Jamal **gained 5** points. To show $-3 + 5$, start at -3 and **move right 5** to add 5. The result is 2.

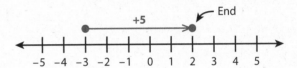

At the end of the contest, the team has 2 points.

When you add two negative numbers, the sum is always a negative number.

When you add a positive number and a negative number, the sign of the sum will be the sign of the number with the greater absolute value.

$$3 + (-4) = -1 \qquad\qquad -3 + 5 = 2$$

$|-4|$ is greater than $|3|$, so the sign of the answer will be the sign of -4.

$|5|$ is greater than $|-3|$, so the sign of the answer will be the sign of 5.

▶ Reflect

1 Describe how to add -8 and 14 on a number line that runs from -10 to 10.

_____

_____

Learn About ▷ **Addition Methods for Integers**

Read the problem below. Then explore different ways to understand how to add positive and negative numbers.

> Ali wants to make bracelets to sell at a craft fair. She borrows money from her sister to buy beads and cord. Ali spends $8.00 on supplies. At the craft fair, Ali makes $17.00 selling her bracelets. How much money does Ali have after she pays back her sister?

▶ **Model It** **You can use a bar model to understand the problem.**

The model shows how much money Ali has after she pays her sister the $8 she borrowed.

17	
?	8

▶ **Model It** **You can use a number line to help understand the problem.**

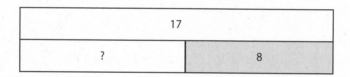

▶ **Model It** **You can use an equation to help understand the problem.**

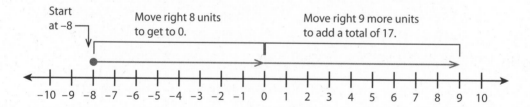

Connect It Now you will solve the problem from the previous page using equations.

2 Use the bar model on the previous page to write an expression using subtraction to represent the amount of money Ali has after the fair. _____
Write the expression using addition. _____

3 How are the expressions you wrote in problem 2 related?

_____

_____

4 What does -8 represent on the number line on the previous page? Why is the number negative? _____

_____

5 Use the number line on the previous page to write an expression to represent the amount of money Ali has after the fair. _____

6 Simplify the expressions you wrote in problem 2 and problem 5 to find the amount of money Ali has left after she pays her sister. Do you get the same answer? Explain.

_____

7 Describe another situation that can be represented by adding a negative number and a positive number. _____

_____

Try It Use what you just learned about adding positive and negative numbers to solve these problems. Write and simplify an expression for each problem. Show your work on a separate sheet of paper.

8 In a trivia game, Joshua gets a score of -4 in the first round and -5 in the second round. What is his total score after the two rounds? _____

9 A balloon is 23 feet below a tree limb. The balloon floats up 19 feet. What is its position relative to the tree limb? _____

Learn About ▷ **Subtraction Methods for Integers**

Read the problem below. Then explore different ways to subtract positive and negative numbers.

Indi, Mark, and Tess each pick a slip of paper with a subtraction expression written on it. The person holding the card with the greatest value wins a prize. Who wins the prize?

Indi	Mark	Tess
$2 - 3$	$-7 - (-4)$	$-1 - (-7)$

▶ **Model It** **You can rewrite the subtraction problems as addition problems and add them on a number line.**

Subtracting a number is the same as adding the opposite of the number.

Indi's slip: **Subtracting 3 is the same as adding −3.**
Start at 2. **Move left 3 units.**

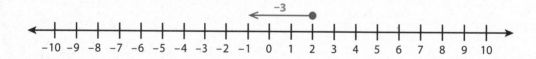

Mark's slip: **Subtracting −4 is the same as adding 4.**
Start at −7. **Move right 4 units.**

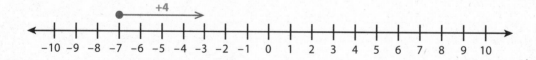

Tess's slip: **Subtracting −7 is the same as adding 7.**
Start at −1. **Move right 7 units.**

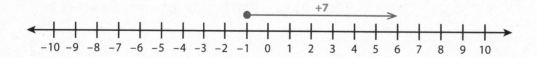

Connect It Now you will solve the problems on the previous page by writing them as addition problems.

10 What is the same about all of the expressions on the previous page?

_____

11 What do you need to do to write a subtraction problem as an addition problem?

_____

12 Write $2 - 3$ as an addition problem. Then simplify the expression. _____

Write $-7 - (-4)$ as an addition problem. Then simplify the expression. _____

Write $-1 - (-7)$ as an addition problem. Then simplify the expression. _____

13 Who has the slip of paper with the greatest value? What is that value? _____

14 Compare the problems on Mark's slip and Tess' slip. When one negative number is subtracted from another negative number, when is the answer positive?

_____

_____

_____

Try It Use what you just learned to solve these problems. Show your work on a separate sheet of paper.

15 Gerry and Jane play a trivia game. Gerry's score is -17 and Jane's score is -24. What is the difference between Gerry's score and Jane's score? _____

16 The table shows the highest and lowest elevations in Louisiana. What is the difference between the elevations?

_____

Elevations in Louisiana	
Location	Elevation (ft)
Mt. Driskill	535
New Orleans	−8

Practice Addition and Subtraction Methods for Integers

Study the example below. Then solve problems 17–19.

Example

Jackie is sitting on a rock 5 feet above the surface of a pond. She drops a stone that falls 8 feet to the bottom of the pond. What is the stone's final position, relative to the surface of the pond?

Look at how you could show your work using a number line.

$5 - 8 = 5 + (-8)$

Solution ___ −3 feet, or 3 feet below the surface of the pond

The stone starts 5 feet above the water's surface and falls 8 feet. A vertical number line helps to picture this situation.

Pair/Share
How else could you solve the problem?

---

17 Kelly's dad compares her running times in a marathon to her times for last year's race. He records whether she has increased or decreased her time for the first three stages of the race. What is the total increase or decrease in Kelly's time? Did she improve her time? Explain.

Show your work.

Kelly's Marathon Times	
Stage	**Time Comparison (in minutes)**
First	4
Second	−7
Third	−3

Does a negative number represent an increase or a decrease in Kelly's time compared to last year?

Pair/Share
Describe other situations you might want to represent with a negative number.

Solution _____

_____

18 A helicopter is 19 meters above the top of a canyon wall. It goes down 27 meters, passing into the canyon, and then goes up 5 meters. What is the new position of the helicopter relative to the top of the canyon wall?

Show your work.

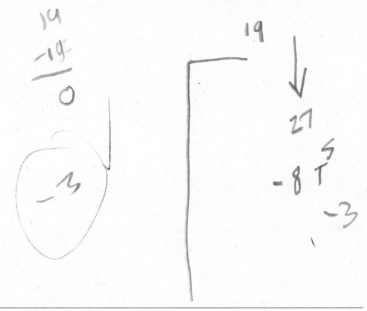

Do you use a positive or a negative number to represent the helicopter going down 27 meters?

Solution _____

💬 **Pair/Share**

What does a negative answer mean in this situation?

---

19 At 7:00 AM the temperature in Wilton was −6°F. By 8:00 AM the temperature was 2°F. What is the difference in the temperature between 8:00 AM and 7:00 AM?

A −8°F

B −4°F

C 4°F

D 8°F

To find the difference between two temperatures, should you add or subtract?

Siri chose **B** as the correct answer. How did she get that answer?

Sha s.... □ subtracted 2

_____

_____

_____

💬 **Pair/Share**

Does Siri's answer make sense? Why or why not?

Practice ▷ Addition and Subtraction Methods for Integers

Solve the problems.

1 A submarine is 50 meters below sea level. It goes up 15 meters, then goes down 40 meters. What is the submarine's new position relative to sea level?

A −105 meters

B −75 meters

C −35 meters

D 25 meters

2 The table shows the temperatures and wind-chill temperatures in four towns.

Town	Actual Temperature	Wind-Chill Temperature
Easton	−3°F	−13°F
Mariton	0°F	−15°F
Pine Hills	10°F	−10°F
West Falls	2°F	−17°F

Which town had the **greatest** difference between the actual temperature and the wind-chill temperature?

A Easton

B Mariton

C Pine Hills

D West Falls

3 Look at the equations below. Choose *True* or *False* for each equation.

a. $-7 - 5 + 3 = 1$ ☐ True ☐ False

b. $-(9 + 11) + 1 = -1$ ☐ True ☐ False

c. $24 - (-6) - 6 = 24$ ☐ True ☐ False

d. $12 + (-8) - 1 = 3$ ☐ True ☐ False

e. $-|2 - 7| + 5 = 0$ ☐ True ☐ False

4 Which situation could the numeric expression $-8 + 10$ represent? Select all that apply.

A An atom has a positive charge because it contains 8 electrons that each have a charge of -1 and 10 protons that each have a charge of $+1$.

B Janice sold 8 goldfish for a total of $10. Therefore, she made a profit of $2.

C At a bus stop, 8 people got off the bus and 10 people got on. This means that the number of passengers increased by 2.

D The temperature dropped 8 degrees and then another 10 degrees. The temperature is now -18 degrees.

5 In golf, each hole has a score called par, which is the number of strokes a good golfer should take to get the ball in the hole. Scores that are under par are represented by a negative number. The table shows the golf scores for team members in a golf tournament. If the team's total score is -32, what is Curran's score?

Golfer	Score
Rose	-9
Garcia	-15
Curran	?

Answer _____

6 Austin is watching a football game. His team loses 9 yards and then gains 5 yards. He doesn't watch the next play, but afterwards he sees that his team now has a total loss of 1 yard. How many yards did the team gain or lose on the play Austin missed?

Answer _____

 **Self Check** Go back and see what you can check off on the Self Check on page 1.

Multiply and Divide Positive and Negative Integers

Use What You Know

In Lessons 1–3, you learned that adding integers is a lot like adding and subtracting whole numbers. Take a look at this problem.

What numbers complete Table 1? What numbers complete Table 2?

Table 1		Table 2	
Multiplication	**Product**	**Multiplication**	**Product**
$3 \cdot 3$	9	$-3 \cdot 3$	
$3 \cdot 2$	6	$-3 \cdot 2$	-6
$3 \cdot 1$	3	$-3 \cdot 1$	-3
$3 \cdot 0$	0	$-3 \cdot 0$	
$3 \cdot (-1)$		$-3 \cdot (-1)$	
$3 \cdot (-2)$		$-3 \cdot (-2)$	
$3 \cdot (-3)$		$-3 \cdot (-3)$	

Use the math you already know to solve the problem.

a. Look for a pattern in the products in Table 1. Each product decreases by _____.

b. I can fill Table 1 by adding _____ to each product. Then fill Table 1.

c. Why can you use your entry in Table 1 for $3 \cdot (-3)$ to find the product for $-3 \cdot 3$ in Table 2?

_____

d. Look for a pattern in the products in Table 2. Each product increases by _____.

e. I can fill Table 2 by adding _____ to each product. Then fill Table 2.

f. What do you notice about the factors that result in a negative product?

_____

g. What do you notice about the product when both factors are negative?

_____

Multiplying integers is a lot like multiplying whole numbers. You can use what you know about the properties of operations and repeated addition to multiply integers.

Think about these problems:

$-3 \cdot 1 = ?$	Use the identity property.	$-3 \cdot 1 = -3$
$-3 \cdot 0 = ?$	Use the zero product property.	$-3 \cdot 0 = 0$
$-3 \cdot 3 = ?$	Use the commutative property. Multiplying 3 groups of (-3) is the same as adding 3 groups of -3.	$-3 \cdot 3 = 3 \cdot (-3)$ $3 \cdot (-3) = (-3) + (-3) + (-3) = -9$

You can use the distributive property to show why you get a positive product when you multiply two negative numbers. You know $-3 \cdot 3 = -9$.
One way you can write $-3 \cdot 3$ is to think of it as $-3 \cdot [5 + (-2)]$.

	Write 3 as $[5 + (-2)]$.	$-3 \cdot 3 = -3 \cdot [5 + (-2)]$
	Use the distributive property.	$-9 = (-3)(5) + (-3)(-2)$.
Think:	$(-3)(5)$ is the same as $5(-3)$ or $(-3) + (-3) + (-3) + (-3) + (-3)$ $= -15$	$-9 = -15 + (-3)(-2)$

Since $-9 = -15 + 6$, we know that $(-3)(-2) = 6$.
So when you multiply two negative numbers, the product is a positive number.

You can use these facts to find products when there are more than two negative numbers.

$(-3) \cdot (-3) \cdot (-3) =$ $(-3) \cdot (-3) \cdot (-3) \cdot (-3) =$

$9 \cdot (-3) = -27$ $9 \cdot 9 = 81$

▶ Reflect

1 For each statement, tell whether the product is *positive* or *negative*:

When you multiply a positive integer by a negative integer or a negative integer by a positive

integer, the product is _____.

When you multiply a negative integer by a negative integer, the product is _____.

When you multiply an even number of negative integers, the product is _____.

When you multiply an odd number of negative integers, the product is _____.

Learn About Multiplying Integers

Read the problem below. Then explore different ways to understand multiplying integers.

> Lisa owes $2 to each of 6 friends. What integer represents Lisa's debt?

▶ **Model It** **You can use groups to help understand the problem.**

Lisa owes **$2** to each of **6** friends. You can write that as **6 groups** of (−2).

6 groups of (−2) = (−2) + (−2) + (−2) + (−2) + (−2) + (−2) = −12

▶ **Model It** **You can also use models to understand the problem.**

The following number line shows the amount Lisa owes her friends.

Start at 0 and make **6** jumps of **−2**.

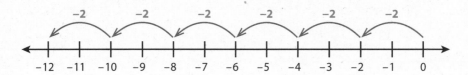

Connect It Now you will solve the problem from the previous page using equations.

2 What number represents the amount Lisa owes each friend? _____

3 Is the amount positive or negative? Why?

_____

_____

4 How many friends does Lisa owe? _____

5 Complete the phrase to show how much Lisa owes.

_____ groups of _____

6 Rewrite the addition of groups as multiplication of groups.

$(-2) + (-2) + (-2) + (-2) + (-2) + (-2) =$ _____ $\cdot (-2)$

7 Adding 6 groups of (-2) is the same as _____ 6 and (-2).

8 Complete the multiplication to find the integer that represents Lisa's total debt.

$6 \cdot (-2) =$ _____

9 Explain how you can use the rules of multiplying a positive number by a negative number to check that your answer has the correct sign.

_____

_____

Try It Use what you just learned to solve these problems. Show your work on a separate sheet of paper.

10 $-8 \cdot 12 =$ _____

11 A crack in a water tank leaks 7 gallons of water each hour. After 9 hours, what is the change in the volume of water in the tank due to the leak?

_____

Lesson 4 Multiply and Divide Positive and Negative Integers   **27**

Learn About ▸ **Dividing Integers**

Read the problem below. Then explore different ways to understand dividing integers.

> Rosa is at the top of a climbing wall. She descends 48 feet of the wall in 6 equal stages. What number represents the change in Rosa's position at each stage?

▶ **Picture It** **You can use a diagram to help you understand the problem.**

The following diagram shows the change in Rosa's position at each stage. The top of the wall is the starting or 0 position.

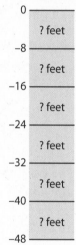

Rosa's Change in Position

▶ **Model It** **You can also use division to help you understand the problem.**

Total change (in feet)	÷	Number of stages	=	Change in each stage (in feet)
−48	÷	6	=	?

Connect It   Now you will solve the problem from the previous page by reasoning about division.

12 Rewrite Rosa's division problem from the previous page as a multiplication problem.

$-48 \div 6 = ?$ ➡️ $6 \cdot ? =$ _____

13 Think about what you know about multiplying positive and negative integers. Will the missing number in the multiplication problem be positive or negative? Why?

_____

_____

14 Solve to find the change in Rosa's position at each stage.

$6 \cdot$ _____ $= -48$

The change in position at each stage is _____ feet.

15 Now look at these division problems. Rewrite each as multiplication. Then use multiplication rules to decide whether the missing number is positive or negative.

$-15 \div 3 = ?$ _____ $\cdot ? =$ _____ The missing number is _____.

$-15 \div (-3) = ?$ _____ $\cdot ? =$ _____ The missing number is _____.

$15 \div (-3) = ?$ _____ $\cdot ? =$ _____ The missing number is _____.

16 Use the multiplication rules to complete these statements about division with integers.

When you divide a negative integer by a positive integer, the quotient is _____.

When you divide a negative integer by a negative integer, the quotient is _____.

When you divide a positive integer by a negative integer, the quotient is _____.

Try It   Use what you just learned to solve these problems. Show your work on a separate sheet of paper.

17 $54 \div (-9) =$ _____

18 A glider descends 240 meters in 12 seconds. What is the average change in elevation per second?

_____

Practice ▶ **Multiplying and Dividing Integers**

Study the example below. Then solve problems 19–21.

Example

Paul, Hayden, and Alex each have a card with a multiplication sentence written on it. Paul thinks each card has a different solution. Hayden thinks each card has the same solution. Alex thinks only two cards have the same solution. Who is correct?

$$-4 \cdot 3 = ?$$

$$4 \cdot (-3) = ?$$

$$-4 \cdot (-3) = ?$$

The student used multiplication rules to check the sign for each solution.

Look at how you could show your work using multiplication rules.

Equation	Rule	Solution
$-4 \cdot 3 = ?$	negative · positive = negative	-12
$4 \cdot (-3) = ?$	positive · negative = negative	-12
$-4 \cdot (-3) = ?$	negative · negative = positive	$+12$

Solution _Alex is correct. Only two cards have the same solution, −12._

Pair/Share
How could you use addition of groups to show that $4 \cdot (-3) = -12$?

---

19 A movie rental company deducts $7 from Serena's account every month for a year. After 1 year, how much do movie rental fees change Serena's account?

Show your work.

Will your answer be positive or negative?

Pair/Share
How can you check that your answer is reasonable?

Solution _____

20 The table shows the low temperatures in Alto for 5 days. What is the average low temperature?

Daily Low Temperature in Alto	
Day	**Low Temperature**
1	−4°F
2	−7°F
3	−13°F
4	−5°F
5	−5°F

Show your work.

Solution _____

To find the average of a set of numbers, do you multiply or divide?

Pair/Share
How did you and your partner decide what step to do first?

---

21 Which equation has a negative solution?

A $-6 \div (-2) = \square$

B $-6 + (-2) = \square$

C $-2 \cdot (-6) = \square$

D $-2 - (-6) = \square$

Seth chose **C** as the correct answer. How did he get that answer?

_____

_____

_____

How can you use the multiplication rules to help you solve this problem?

Pair/Share
How did you and your partner choose your answer?

Practice › Multiplying and Dividing Integers

Solve the problems.

1 Which multiplication equation is *false*?

A $(-a) \cdot (-1) = (-a)$

B $(-a) \cdot 0 = 0$

C $(-a) \cdot 1 = (-a)$

D $(-a) \cdot b = b \cdot (-a)$

2 The lowest elevation in Long Beach, California, is 7 feet below sea level. The elevation of Death Valley is about 40 times lower than the elevation of Long Beach. What is the approximate elevation of Death Valley?

A -280 feet

B -47 feet

C -33 feet

D -6 feet

3 Draw a line from each expression to the word problem it could represent.

-12×4	A football team loses a total of 12 yards in 4 plays. On average, how many yards did the team move per play?
12×4	The temperature of the ocean water dropped 4 degrees every hour. After 12 hours, what was the change in the water temperature?
$12 \times (-4)$	A garden consists of 12 rose bushes in each of 4 rows. How many rose bushes does the garden have altogether?
$-3 \times (-4)$	Every second, a snail crawls 12 millimeters down a hole. What is the snail's change in position after 4 seconds?
$-12 \div 4$	During a drought, a pond's fish population decreased by 3 for every meter drop in the pond's water level. At that rate, how many fish died once the water level dropped 4 meters?

4 Write each expression under the category that correctly describes the number to which the expression simplifies.

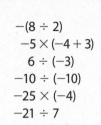

$$-(8 \div 2)$$
$$-5 \times (-4 + 3)$$
$$6 \div (-3)$$
$$-10 \div (-10)$$
$$-25 \times (-4)$$
$$-21 \div 7$$

A negative number	A positive number

5 Marc's elevation decreases by 350 meters as he rides his bike down to the bottom of a hill. He did the ride in 5 equal stages. How much did Marc's elevation change during each stage?

Show your work.

Answer _____

6 Hugh is playing a game. He spins each spinner and then multiplies the numbers to find the product.

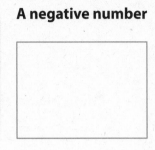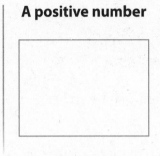

Spinner A — -4, -2, 0, 5
Spinner B — -3, -1, -6, 0

Part A Give an example of two numbers Hugh could spin to get a positive product.

Answer _____

_____

Part B Give an example of two numbers Hugh could spin to get a negative product.

Answer _____

_____

✓ **Self Check** Go back and see what you can check off on the Self Check on page 1.

Use What You Know

You learned that fractions can be written as decimals. Take a look at this problem.

Jenna figured out the cost of different fruits per piece, and wrote the unit costs as fractions. She wants to write each unit cost as a decimal to show the cost in cents. How can she write these common fractions as decimals?

Fruit	Cost Per Piece in Dollars
strawberry	$\frac{1}{10}$
kiwi	$\frac{1}{5}$
apple	$\frac{1}{4}$
banana	$\frac{1}{2}$
mango	$\frac{3}{4}$

Use the math you already know to solve the problem.

a. Write each fraction as an equivalent fraction with a denominator of 10 or 100.

Unit Fraction	Equivalent Fraction	Decimal
$\frac{1}{10}$	$\frac{}{10}$	
$\frac{1}{5}$	$\frac{}{10}$	
$\frac{1}{4}$	$\frac{}{100}$	
$\frac{1}{2}$	$\frac{}{10}$	
$\frac{3}{4}$	$\frac{}{100}$	

b. What about the denominators of the fractions made it convenient to use equivalent fractions as a step in writing them as decimals? _____

_____

_____

▷▷ Find Out More

In real life, fractions and decimals are used to represent weight, money, temperature, time, length, and distance. We often find data represented by fractions that would be easier to work with if they were decimals.

You know that one half is one whole cut into two equal shares. So, $\frac{1}{2}$ means $1 \div 2$, and $\frac{1}{4}$ means $1 \div 4$. You can use division to write any fraction as a decimal.

$\frac{1}{2}$ means $1 \div 2$.

$$\begin{array}{r} 0.5 \\ 2\overline{)1.0} \\ -\,1.0 \\ \hline 0 \end{array}$$

$\frac{1}{4}$ means $1 \div 4$.

$$\begin{array}{r} 0.25 \\ 4\overline{)1.00} \\ -\,8\downarrow \\ \hline 20 \\ 20 \\ \hline 0 \end{array}$$

$\frac{3}{4}$ means $3 \div 4$.

$$\begin{array}{r} 0.75 \\ 4\overline{)3.00} \\ -\,28\downarrow \\ \hline 20 \\ -\,20 \\ \hline 0 \end{array}$$

You can verify that each decimal quotient is correct by multiplying the quotient by the divisor. For example, $\frac{1}{4} = 0.25$ and $0.25 \times 4 = 1$. Or, $\frac{3}{4} = 0.75$ and $0.75 \times 4 = 3$.

The decimal number for each of these fractions has only 1 or 2 digits after the decimal point, but the decimals for some fractions have many more digits, and some never end at all. Look what happens when you divide to find the decimal for $\frac{1}{3}$.

$$\begin{array}{r} 0.333 \\ 3\overline{)1.000} \\ -\,9\downarrow\downarrow \\ \hline 10 \\ -\,9\downarrow \\ \hline 10 \\ -\,9 \\ \hline 1 \end{array}$$

In this lesson, you will learn about both **terminating decimals** such as 0.25 and **repeating decimals** such as 0.333333 . . ., which never end but repeat the same digits over and over.

▶ Reflect

1 Describe how you could find the decimal that is to equivalent to $\frac{3}{15}$ using what you just learned, without doing any long division.

_____

Learn About Using Patterns to Write Fractions as Decimals

Read the problem below. Then explore different ways to understand writing eighths as decimals.

> How do the decimal forms of fractions help you compare their values? Find patterns or relationships among fractions for $\frac{1}{8}$, $\frac{2}{8}$, $\frac{3}{8}$, $\frac{4}{8}$, and $\frac{5}{8}$.

▶ **Picture It** You can use fraction strips to visualize the numbers.

The fraction strips show that each of these fractions is $\frac{1}{8}$ more than the previous fraction.

▶ **Model It** You can use a table of values to help show relationships.

Fraction	Decimal
$\frac{1}{8}$	0.125
$\frac{2}{8}$	0.250
$\frac{3}{8}$	0.375
$\frac{4}{8}$	0.500
$\frac{5}{8}$	0.625
$\frac{6}{8}$	
$\frac{7}{8}$	

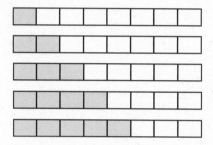

Look for a pattern to think about how to find the decimal forms of $\frac{6}{8}$ and $\frac{7}{8}$.

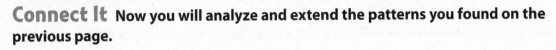

Connect It Now you will analyze and extend the patterns you found on the previous page.

2 Describe the pattern in the decimal numbers in the table in *Model It*. Tell how the numbers change and why.

_____

_____

3 Extend this pattern to write $\frac{6}{8}$ and $\frac{7}{8}$ as decimals in the table. Explain your thinking.

_____

4 In the chart below, write the decimal form of the unit fractions $\frac{1}{8}$, $\frac{1}{4}$, and $\frac{1}{2}$.

Unit Fraction	Decimal
$\frac{1}{8}$	
$\frac{1}{4}$	
$\frac{1}{2}$	

5 Explain how you could get from one row to the next by multiplying.

_____

6 Explain how you could build on knowing the decimal form of $\frac{1}{5}$, which you found in *Reflect*, to find the decimal form of $\frac{3}{5}$. Then write the decimal. _____

_____

Try It Use what you just learned about writing fractions as decimals to solve these problems. Show your work on a separate sheet of paper.

7 Isaiah knows that $\frac{1}{4}$ is written 0.25 as a decimal. How can he find a decimal for $\frac{5}{4}$

without dividing? _____

8 What is another way Isaiah can figure out the decimal for $\frac{5}{4}$ without dividing?

_____

_____

Learn About ⟩ **Terminating and Repeating Decimals**

Read the problem below. Then explore different ways to understand writing sixths as decimals.

Juan sells banana bread by weight. He cuts a 1-lb loaf of banana bread into 6 equal slices. He wants to complete the table showing the total weight for the various numbers of slices. What decimals will he write in the table?

Number of Slices	Total Weight (pounds)
1	
2	
3	
4	
5	
6	1.0

▶ **Estimate It** **You can use estimation to understand the problem.**

$\frac{1}{6}$ is between $\frac{1}{8}$ and $\frac{1}{5}$, so it is between 0.125 and 0.2.

▶ **Model It** **You can use division to find the decimal for $\frac{1}{6}$.**

Fraction	Decimal
$\frac{1}{6}$	0.1666...
$\frac{2}{6}$	
$\frac{3}{6}$	0.5
$\frac{4}{6}$	
$\frac{5}{6}$	
$\frac{6}{6}$	1.0

$$
\begin{array}{r}
0.1666 \\
6\overline{)1.0000} \\
-\underline{6} \\
40 \\
-\underline{36} \\
40 \\
-\underline{36} \\
40 \\
-\underline{36} \\
4
\end{array}
$$

Connect It Now you will find decimals for sixths, ninths, and thirds using division and patterns.

9 Continue the division of 1 ÷ 6 on the previous page for 2 more decimal places. What do you notice? _____

_____

10 Explain why the decimal for $\frac{1}{6}$ is called a repeating decimal.

_____

_____

> To show a repeating decimal, you write a bar over the digit or digits that repeat. In this decimal, the digit 6 repeats. $\frac{1}{6} = 0.1\overline{6}$

11 Complete the chart in *Model It* on the previous page. Describe and explain the relationship between the decimals for $\frac{2}{6}$ and $\frac{4}{6}$.

_____

_____

12 Divide to write $\frac{1}{9}$ as a decimal. Continue to 3 decimal places. Show your work in the space to the right. _____

13 How can you use the fact that $\frac{1}{3} = \frac{3}{9}$ to write the decimal for $\frac{1}{3}$? What is that decimal?

_____

_____

Try It Use what you just learned to solve these problems. Show your work on a separate sheet of paper.

14 Predict the decimal for $\frac{4}{9}$. Divide to check your prediction, and describe the results.

_____

_____

15 How can you find the decimal for $\frac{12}{9}$? What is the decimal?

_____

_____

Practice ▸ Writing Fractions as Terminating and Repeating Decimals

Study the example below. Then solve problems 16–18.

Example

Reno needs $\frac{8}{3}$ ounces of milk for a dessert recipe. His kitchen scale shows he has 2.6 ounces of milk. Does he have more or less than $\frac{8}{3}$ ounces?

Look at how you could show your work using division.

$$\frac{8}{3} = 8 \div 3$$

$$
\begin{array}{r}
2.666 \\
3\overline{)8.000} \\
-6 \\
\hline
20 \\
-18 \\
\hline
20 \\
-18 \\
\hline
20 \\
-18 \\
\hline
2 \\
\end{array}
$$

Reno needs $2.\overline{6}$ ounces.

$2.\overline{6} > 2.6$

Solution <u>Reno has just a little less than $\frac{8}{3}$ ounces.</u>

The student rewrote the fraction as a decimal using division.

 Pair/Share
The division did not end in 0. Why did the student stop dividing?

---

16 Anna saves $\frac{5}{8}$ of her money. What percent of her money does Anna save?

Show your work.

Remember, you can write a decimal as a percent. Move the decimal point two places to the right to write a percent.

 Pair/Share
What method did you use to rewrite the fraction as a decimal?

Solution _____

17 Use division to find the decimal equivalent for $\frac{1}{7}$. Be sure to continue dividing until the decimal terminates or begins to repeat.

Show your work.

I know $\frac{1}{7}$ is more than $\frac{1}{8}$ and less than $\frac{1}{6}$, so my answer will be between 0.125 and $0.1\overline{6}$.

Solution _____

 Pair/Share
How far do you need to continue the division of 1 by 7 to know the answer?

18 Audrey is practicing basketball. She makes a basket from the free-throw line 8 out of 25 shots. Which decimal shows the fraction of Audrey's shots that result in baskets? Circle the letter of the correct answer.

A 3.2

B 3.125

C 0.32

D 0.3125

Will your answer be greater than 1 or less than 1?

Jorge chose **B** as the correct answer. How did he get that answer?

_____

_____

_____

 Pair/Share
When you write a repeating decimal, how do you decide where to draw the bar?

Practice ▶ **Writing Fractions as Terminating and Repeating Decimals**

Solve the problems.

1 Joe's apple weighs $\frac{4}{5}$ lb. Marta's apple weighs 0.5 lb. How much **more** does Joe's apple weigh than Marta's?

A 0.3 lb   C 0.8 lb

B 0.75 lb   D 1.25 lb

2 At 2:30 AM the temperature in Joelle is 3°F. The temperature drops $\frac{3}{4}$ of a degree in 30 minutes. What is the temperature in Joelle at 3:00 AM?

A 2.$\overline{2}$°F   C 3.75°F

B 2.25°F   D 3.$\overline{7}$°F

3 Write each number in the appropriate box to show its placement along the number line.

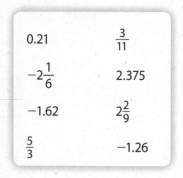

0.21 $\frac{3}{11}$

$-2\frac{1}{6}$ 2.375

-1.62 $2\frac{2}{9}$

$\frac{5}{3}$ -1.26

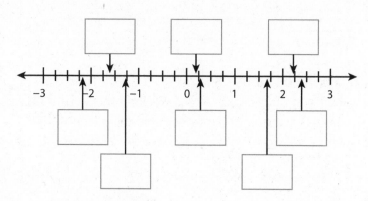

4 Determine whether the decimal for each fraction will terminate or repeat. Choose *Terminates* or *Repeats* for each fraction.

a. $\frac{4}{3}$ ☐ Terminates   ☐ Repeats

b. $\frac{3}{9}$ ☐ Terminates   ☐ Repeats

c. $\frac{9}{15}$ ☐ Terminates   ☐ Repeats

d. $\frac{10}{18}$ ☐ Terminates   ☐ Repeats

5 Bill is playing a game. He chooses one fraction card and one decimal card that have the same value. What 2 cards might Bill choose?

Answer Bill could choose the fraction _____ and the decimal _____.

6 The table below shows some decimal equivalents for elevenths.

Fraction	Decimal
$\frac{1}{11}$	$0.\overline{09}$
$\frac{2}{11}$	$0.\overline{18}$
$\frac{3}{11}$	$0.\overline{27}$
$\frac{4}{11}$	
$\frac{5}{11}$	
$\frac{6}{11}$	
$\frac{7}{11}$	

Part A Describe one pattern you see in the repeated digits.

_____

_____

_____

Part B Complete the table. Use division to check one answer.

_____

✓ **Self Check** Go back and see what you can check off on the Self Check on page 1.

⟳ Use What You Know

In Lesson 4, you learned the rules for multiplying and dividing integers. Take a look at this problem.

> Vera is given three fractions. She wants to find the two fractions that have the greatest product. Which two fractions does Vera multiply together to find the greatest product?
>
> $\dfrac{4}{5}$ $-\dfrac{2}{5}$ $-\dfrac{3}{5}$

Use the math you already know to solve the problem. Begin by solving a simpler problem.

a. Use what you know about multiplying and dividing integers to find the product of $-\dfrac{10}{5} \times \dfrac{20}{5}$. You can think of $-\dfrac{10}{5} \times \dfrac{20}{5}$ as -2×4, which equals _____.

b. Find the product of $-\dfrac{10}{5} \times \left(-\dfrac{15}{5}\right)$. Think of $-\dfrac{10}{5} \times \left(-\dfrac{15}{5}\right)$ as _____ $\times$ _____ which equals _____.

c. Think about multiplying $-\dfrac{2}{5} \times \left(-\dfrac{3}{5}\right)$. Will the product be positive or negative? Explain your reasoning. _____

_____

_____

d. Explain how you can use the rules you know for multiplying positive and negative integers to multiply positive and negative fractions.

_____

_____

_____

_____

In previous lessons you performed operations with integers. Now you will learn about performing operations with other types of rational numbers. A **rational number** is a number that can be written as the quotient of two integers. Rational numbers include positive and negative fractions and decimals, and also integers since an integer can be written as a fraction with 1 as the denominator: $-6 = -\frac{6}{1}$.

When you multiply positive and negative fractions, you multiply the numerator by the numerator and then the denominator by the denominator, all the while using the rules for multiplying integers.

In the problem on the previous page, you multiply the fractions to find the greatest product.

$$-\frac{3}{5} \times \frac{4}{5} = -\frac{12}{25} \qquad \frac{4}{5} \times \left(-\frac{2}{5}\right) = -\frac{8}{25} \qquad -\frac{3}{5} \times \left(-\frac{2}{5}\right) = \frac{6}{25}$$

So, $-\frac{3}{5} \times \left(-\frac{2}{5}\right)$ has the greatest product. It is the only product that is a positive number.

You also use the rules for multiplying positive and negative numbers when you divide fractions. Look at the examples below.

$$-\frac{2}{5} \div \frac{4}{5} = -\frac{2}{5} \times \frac{5}{4} \qquad\qquad -\frac{3}{10} \div \left(-\frac{4}{5}\right) = -\frac{3}{10} \times \left(-\frac{5}{4}\right)$$
$$= -\frac{10}{20} \qquad\qquad\qquad\qquad\qquad = \frac{15}{40}$$
$$= -\frac{1}{2} \qquad\qquad\qquad\qquad\qquad\quad = \frac{3}{8}$$

The rules for multiplying and dividing integers also apply to decimals.

$$-3.5 \times (-2.4) = 8.4 \qquad 3.5 \times (-2.4) = -8.4 \qquad -3.5 \times 2.4 = -8.4$$

$$-4.25 \div (-0.2) = 21.25 \qquad 4.25 \div (-0.2) = -21.25 \qquad -4.25 \div 0.2 = -21.25$$

▶ **Reflect**

1 How are the rules for dividing two negative fractions related to the rules for multiplying two negative fractions? Will the answer be positive or negative? Explain.

_____

_____

_____

_____

_____

Learn About ▶ **Multiplying Rational Numbers**

Read the problem below. Then explore different ways to understand it.

Alicia, Emma, and Nick dive into an extremely deep pool. Alicia dives to a position of $-\frac{9}{4}$ yards relative to the surface of the water. Emma dives to a position twice as deep as Alicia. Nick dives to a position $\frac{2}{3}$ as deep as Alicia. What are Emma's and Nick's positions, relative to the surface of the water?

▶ **Picture It** **You can use models to understand the problem.**

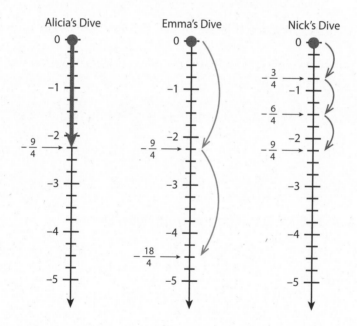

▶ **Model It** **You can also use multiplication to understand the problem.**

Alicia's position: $-\frac{9}{4}$ yards

Emma's position: $2 \times$ Alicia's position $= 2 \times \left(-\frac{9}{4}\right)$ yards

Nick's position: $\frac{2}{3} \times$ Alicia's position $= \frac{2}{3} \times \left(-\frac{9}{4}\right)$ yards

Connect It Now you will solve the problem on the previous page.

2 Look at the number line representing Emma's dive. What do the two arrows represent?

_____

_____

3 Look at *Model It*. Why do you multiply Alicia's position by 2 to find Emma's position?

_____

4 Look at the number line representing Nick's dive. Why are there three equal arrows ending at the position of Alicia's dive? How will you use the arrows to find Nick's position?

_____

_____

_____

5 Look at *Model It*. Why do you multiply Alicia's position by $\frac{2}{3}$ to find Nick's position?

_____

6 Evaluate the products to find Emma's position and Nick's position.

$2 \times \left(-\frac{9}{4}\right) = $ _____ $\frac{2}{3} \times \left(-\frac{9}{4}\right) = $ _____

7 Explain how you can use the rules for multiplying positive and negative numbers to check that your answers to problem 6 have the correct sign.

_____

Try It Use what you just learned to solve these problems. Show your work on a separate sheet of paper.

8 The temperature at noon is 0°C. The temperature changes by $-\frac{3}{2}$°C every hour for 4 hours. Write an expression to represent this situation. What is the temperature at 4:00 PM?

_____

9 $-\frac{5}{6} \times \left(-\frac{3}{10}\right) = $ _____

Learn About **Dividing Rational Numbers**

Read the problem below. Then explore different ways to understand it.

> The volume of water in Pete's pool is changing by −0.05 gallon per hour due to a leak. How many hours will it take for the volume of water in the pool to change by a total of −0.3 gallon?

▶ **Picture It** **You can use a bar model to understand the problem.**

−0.1		−0.1		−0.1	
−0.05	−0.05	−0.05	−0.05	−0.05	−0.05

▶ **Model It** **You can use repeated subtraction to help understand the problem.**

Total change in water volume	=	Sum of the changes in water volume each hour

$$-0.3 = 0.05 + (-0.05) + (-0.05) + (-0.05) + (-0.05) + (-0.05)$$

▶ **Model It** **You can use division to help understand the problem.**

Total change in water volume	÷	Changes in water volume each hour	=	Number of hours

$$-0.3 \div (-0.05) = ?$$

Connect It Now you will solve the problem from the previous page using division.

10 Look at *Picture It*. What do the three bars labeled −0.1 represent? What do the bars labeled −0.05 represent? _____

_____

_____

11 Why are the bars in *Picture It* labeled with negative numbers? _____

_____

_____

12 Look at *Model It*. How do you decide how many times to add −0.05?

_____

13 How many hours will it take for the volume of water in the pool to change by a total of −0.3 gallon? _____

14 Explain how you can use the rules for dividing a negative number by a negative number to determine the sign of the quotient −0.3 ÷ (−0.05).

_____

_____

Try It Use what you just learned to solve these problems. Show your work on a separate sheet of paper.

15 Rebecca's bank statement shows a change of −$1.50 in her account each week. How many weeks will it take before the total change is −$12? _____

16 The elevation of a small submarine changes by $-\frac{3}{8}$ mile after each exploration. After how many explorations will the submarine's elevation have changed by $-1\frac{1}{2}$ miles?

_____

Practice **Multiplying and Dividing Rational Numbers**

Study the example below. Then solve problems 17–19.

Example

What is the product of these three fractions: $-\frac{3}{8}$, $-\frac{2}{3}$, $-\frac{5}{2}$?

Look at how you could show your work using multiplication.

$$\left(-\frac{3}{8}\right) \times \left(-\frac{2}{3}\right) \times \left(-\frac{5}{2}\right) = ?$$

$$\left(+\frac{6}{24}\right) \times \left(-\frac{5}{2}\right) = ?$$

$$-\frac{30}{48} = -\frac{5}{8}$$

Solution $-\frac{5}{8}$

The student multiplies the first two fractions, then multiplies by the third fraction.

Pair/Share
Use multiplication rules to confirm that the answer should be negative.

---

17 Lily records the change in her dog's weight over 4 weeks.

My Dog's Weight Change				
Week	1	2	3	4
Weight Change (in pounds)	$-\frac{3}{16}$	$\frac{1}{16}$	$-\frac{5}{16}$	$-\frac{1}{16}$

What is the dog's average weekly weight change?

Show your work.

To find the average of a set of numbers, do you multiply or divide?

Pair/Share
Discuss what step you decided to take first in solving this problem.

Solution

18 Mitch is cutting wood to make a garden marker. Each garden marker changes the length of the piece of wood by −0.8 foot. The length of wood changes by a total of −4$\frac{4}{5}$ feet after Mitch cuts all the garden markers. How many pieces of wood did Mitch cut?

Show your work.

How can you write −0.8 as a fraction?

Pair/Share

Discuss how you can check that your answer is reasonable.

Solution _____

---

19 The amount of shore at a local beach changes an average of −$\frac{3}{4}$ foot each year. What is the change in the amount of shore after 7 years?

A 5$\frac{1}{4}$ feet

B $\frac{3}{28}$ foot

C −$\frac{3}{28}$ foot

D −5$\frac{1}{4}$ feet

If the amount of shore is decreasing, will your answer be positive or negative?

Rashad chose **C** as the correct answer. How did he get that answer?

_____

_____

_____

Pair/Share

Does Rashad's answer make sense? Why or why not?

_____

Practice Multiplying and Dividing Rational Numbers

Solve the problems.

1 The average of a group of numbers is −0.75. Which statement must be true?

A There must be 4 numbers in the group.

B All of the numbers in the group must be negative.

C The sum of the numbers in the group must be negative.

D The sum of the numbers in the group could be positive.

2 A clogged bathtub drains at a constant rate. The amount of water in the bathtub changes by −3.75 gallons in one hour. What is the change in the amount of water in the bathtub after $\frac{1}{3}$ of an hour?

A −1.25 gallons

B −2.25 gallons

C −6.25 gallons

D −11.25 gallons

3 Mara's family is driving to her grandmother's house. The family travels 239.4 miles between the hours of 9:10 AM to 1:40 PM. What is an equation that Mara can use to determine their average rate of travel, R, rounded to the nearest mile per hour? Use the given numbers and operations to complete an equation.

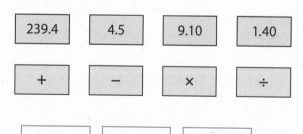

$$\boxed{}\ \boxed{}\ \boxed{} = R$$

4 Victor claims that when $\frac{1}{6}$ is divided by a fraction, the result will always be greater than $\frac{1}{6}$.

Write a number from 1 through 9 in the boxes below to both support and contradict Victor's claim.

Supports Victor's Claim

$\frac{1}{6} \div \dfrac{\square}{\square}$

Contradicts Victor's Claim

$\frac{1}{6} \div \dfrac{\square}{\square}$

5 Frank, Leah, and Tom play a trivia game. Frank's score is −2. Leah's score is $\frac{3}{4}$ of Frank's score. Tom's score is $\frac{2}{3}$ of Leah's score. What is Tom's score?

Show your work.

Answer _____

6 Write all the division problems that will have a negative quotient using two fractions from this list: $-\frac{1}{2}$, $\frac{4}{5}$, $-\frac{3}{8}$. Then evaluate one of your problems. What number must be in all of your problems? Why?

Show your work.

Answer _____

_____

_____

_____

✓ **Self Check** **Go back and see what you can check off on the Self Check on page 1.**

Lesson 7 👥 **Introduction**

Add and Subtract Rational Numbers

7.NS.A.1a
7.NS.A.1b
7.NS.A.1c
7.NS.A.1d

Ⓖ Use What You Know

In Lessons 1–3, you learned about adding and subtracting integers. Take a look at this problem.

> In science class, Ron recorded $-\frac{3}{10}$°C as the starting temperature of a saltwater solution. To complete his experiment, he needs the temperature of the solution to increase by $\frac{4}{10}$°C. What will Ron record as the ending temperature of the solution?

Use the math you already know to solve the problem.

a. Reread the problem. By how much will the temperature of the saltwater

solution increase? _____°C

b. Write an expression to show how to calculate the final temperature of the solution.

_____

c. Explain how you would add $-3 + 4$.

_____

d. Look at the number line below. If you start at -3 tenths of a unit and then move right 4 tenths of a unit, where do you end up?

_____

e. What is $-\frac{3}{10} + \frac{4}{10}$? _____

f. What is the ending temperature for the solution? _____°C

g. Explain how adding $-\frac{3}{10} + \frac{4}{10}$ is like adding $-3 + 4$.

_____

_____

The idea behind adding positive and negative fractions and decimals is the same as the idea behind adding integers.

You can use number lines to show addition of fractions or decimals.

$$-\frac{3}{10} + \frac{4}{10} = \frac{-3+4}{10} = \frac{1}{10}$$

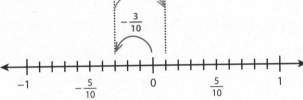

So, $-0.3 + 0.4 = 0.1$.

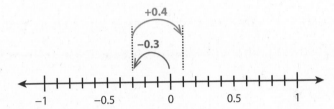

Subtracting positive and negative fractions and decimals is also similar to subtracting integers.

How can you subtract $\frac{3}{8} - \frac{5}{8}$?

First rewrite the subtraction problem as an addition problem using the additive inverse.

$$\frac{3}{8} - \frac{5}{8} = \frac{3}{8} + \left(-\frac{5}{8}\right)$$

You can use a number line to show the problem.

$$\frac{3}{8} + \left(-\frac{5}{8}\right) = \frac{3+(-5)}{8} = -\frac{2}{8}$$

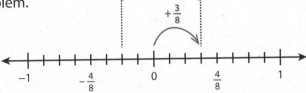

▶ **Reflect**

1 How is adding positive and negative fractions similar to adding integers? How is it different?

_____

_____

_____

_____

_____

Learn About ▶ Adding Negative Fractions

Read the problem below. Then explore different ways to understand adding negative fractions.

> A birdbath is filled to the top. On Day 1, the volume of water in the bowl decreases by $\frac{7}{8}$ cup. On Day 2, the volume of water in the bowl decreases by $\frac{3}{4}$ cup. What number represents the total change in the volume of water in the bowl after two days?

▶ **Picture It** **You can use a number line to help add negative fractions.**

The following number line shows the decrease in the volume of water on Day 1 and Day 2.

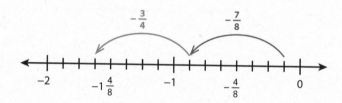

▶ **Model It** **You can use equations to help add negative fractions.**

Amount of water missing at start of Day 1	+	Change in volume on Day 1	=	Overall change in volume at end of Day 1
0	+	$\left(-\frac{7}{8}\right)$	=	?

Overall change in volume at end of Day 1	+	Change in volume on Day 2	=	Overall change in volume at end of Day 2
$-\frac{7}{8}$	+	$\left(-\frac{3}{4}\right)$	=	?

Connect It Now you will solve the problem from the previous page.

2 Think about the expression $-\frac{7}{8} + \left(-\frac{3}{4}\right)$.

What do you need to do before you can add the fractions?

_____

3 Evaluate $-\frac{7}{8} + \left(-\frac{3}{4}\right)$. _____

4 What quantity represents the total change in the volume of water in the birdbath after two days? Write your answer as a mixed number.

_____

5 Look at the problem on the previous page. What does a negative answer mean?

_____

6 How is adding two negative fractions like adding two positive fractions, and how is it different?

_____

_____

_____

_____

7 How is adding two negative fractions similar to adding two negative integers?

_____

_____

Try It Use what you just learned to solve these problems. Show your work on a separate sheet of paper.

8 $-2\frac{1}{2} - 2\frac{1}{2} = $ _____

9 Susan's cat loses $1\frac{1}{4}$ pounds. Then it loses another $\frac{1}{8}$ pound. What is the total change in

the cat's weight? _____

Learn About ▶ ## Adding and Subtracting Rational Numbers

Read the problem below. Then explore different ways to understand adding or subtracting any rational numbers.

> Julia is playing a computer game. To enter a new quest she has to pay a "tax" of 2.5 points, but she expects to earn 7.5 points. For each quest, how many points can she gain overall?

▶ **Picture It** **You can use a number line to help add or subtract rational numbers.**

The following number line shows the **loss of 2.5 points** and **the gain of 7.5 points**.

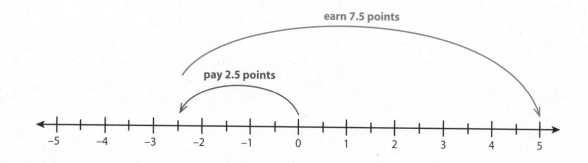

▶ **Model It** **You can use an equation to help add or subtract rational numbers.**

$-2.5 + 7.5 = ?$

Represent the points Julia loses as a negative number, and represent the points she gains as a positive number.

Connect It Now you will solve the problem from the previous page.

10 Think about a loss of 2.5 and a gain of 7.5. Explain how you know whether Julia's overall result will be a gain or a loss, and whether the result should be represented as positive or negative.

_____

_____

11 How can you determine the difference between the gain and the loss?

_____

12 How does knowing the difference between the gain and the loss tell you the overall result?

_____

_____

13 What is $-2.5 + 7.5$? _____ What is $-2\frac{1}{2} + 7\frac{1}{2}$? _____

14 Explain how you can find the sum when you are adding a positive and a negative decimal or fraction. Include how to know whether the sum is positive or negative.

_____

_____

_____

_____

15 Explain how to add the additive inverse to find the value of an expression such as $-4\frac{1}{4} - \left(-2\frac{1}{4}\right)$.

_____

_____

_____

Try It Use what you just learned to solve these problems. Show your work on a separate sheet of paper.

16 What is $-4\frac{1}{2} + 7\frac{1}{2}$? _____

17 What is $2.5 + (-3.5)$? _____

Adding and Subtracting Rational Numbers

Study the example below. Then solve problems 18–20.

Example

Solve the equation. Simplify your answer.

$$\frac{2}{3} - \frac{11}{12} = \square$$

Look at how you could show your work using equations.

$$\frac{2}{3} - \frac{11}{12} = \frac{2}{3} + \left(-\frac{11}{12}\right)$$

$$= \frac{8}{12} + \left(-\frac{11}{12}\right)$$

$$= \frac{8 + (-11)}{12} = -\frac{3}{12} = -\frac{1}{4}$$

Solution $-\frac{3}{12}$, or $-\frac{1}{4}$

The student rewrote the subtraction as addition, found a common denominator, then added the numerators.

 Pair/Share

How could you use a number line to check your answer?

---

18 At midnight, the temperature in Alto is −3.8°C. The wind chill makes the temperature feel 5.6°C colder than the actual temperature. What is the wind-chill temperature?

Show your work.

Will your answer be positive or negative? How do you know?

 Pair/Share

How did you and your partner choose which operation to use?

Solution _____

4 Is each expression equivalent to $\frac{5}{8} - \frac{3}{4}\left(8 - \frac{1}{3}\right) + 1$? Select *Yes* or *No* for each expression.

a. $-\frac{33}{8}$ ☐ Yes ☐ No

b. $-\frac{35}{8}$ ☐ Yes ☐ No

c. $-6\frac{7}{8}$ ☐ Yes ☐ No

d. $-4\frac{1}{8}$ ☐ Yes ☐ No

5 Jamal stands on a dock 1.5 meters above the surface of the water. A trout swims 4.8 meters below Jamal. What is the position of the trout compared to the surface of the water?

Show your work.

Answer _____

6 Solve the problem.

Part A Find a number that makes this statement true.

$-2.5 + $ ☐ $ = $ a positive number

Answer _____

Part B Write an equation showing that your answer makes the statement true.

Answer _____

Part C Draw a number line and use arrows to show your equation.

✓ Self Check **Go back and see what you can check off on the Self Check on page 1.**

Solve Problems with Rational Numbers

Ⓖ Use What You Know

In Lessons 6 and 7 you learned to add, subtract, multiply, and divide rational numbers. In this lesson you will learn to estimate answers to more difficult problems. Take a look at this problem.

> Each morning a gardener uses $24\frac{3}{4}$ gallons of water from a barrel. Each afternoon, she adds $15\frac{1}{4}$ gallons of water to the barrel. By how much has the volume of water in the barrel changed after 5 days?

Use the math you already know to solve the problem.

a. Complete the table. Write the actual change in water volume each morning and afternoon. Then use integers to approximate the change in water volume each day.

	Actual Change	Approximate Change
Change in water volume each morning		
Change in water volume each afternoon		

b. Write an equation to show each situation.

approximate change in volume for 1 day

approximate change in volume for 5 days

_____

_____

actual change in volume for 1 day

actual change in volume for 5 days

_____

_____

c. Explain how integer approximations can help you check the answer to the problem.

_____

_____

_____

Adding and subtracting rational numbers such as fractions and decimals can sometimes be hard to visualize. **Approximations** can help you understand the problem, judge the reasonableness of an exact answer, and help you think about whether the answer will be positive, negative, or 0.

It can be easier to visualize the sum $-25 + 15$ than the sum $-24\frac{3}{4} + 15\frac{1}{4}$.

Knowing the sum should be about -10 helps you check your fraction arithmetic and the sign of your answer.

It can be easier to visualize the product $5 \times (-10)$ than the product $5 \times \left(-9\frac{1}{2}\right)$.

Knowing the product will be about -50 helps you check your fraction arithmetic and the sign of your answer.

Sometimes an approximation may just tell you that the answer will be close to 0, but you will need to do the exact calculations to know whether the answer is 0, just above 0, or just below 0.

For example, you might approximate $4\frac{1}{8} + \left(-7\frac{1}{4}\right) + 2\frac{3}{4} = ?$

$$\text{with } 4 + (-7) + 3 = 0.$$

But because you approximated, the actual answer may not be exactly 0. You may not even be sure whether the sum is positive, 0, or negative until you do the calculation.

▶ Reflect

1 Explain how you could use integers to estimate $-28.3 \cdot (-47.9)$.

_____

_____

_____

_____

_____

Read the problem below. Then explore how estimating can be useful when computing with positive and negative decimals.

> Luisa deposits $44.60 into her bank account on Tuesday morning. Tuesday afternoon, she withdraws $26.30 and $21.30. Does Luisa have more or less money on Tuesday night than she did on Monday night? How much more or less?

▶ **Picture It** **You can use a number line to understand the problem.**

You can use the following number line to approximate each amount to the nearest $5.

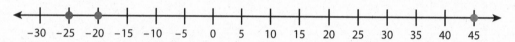

▶ **Model It** **You can also use rounding to help understand the problem.**

You might approximate each amount by rounding to the nearest $1 or to the nearest $5.

Actual Amount	Round to the nearest $1	Round to the nearest $5
44.60	45	45
−26.30	−26	−25
−21.30	−21	−20

Connect It   Now you will solve the problem from the previous page using estimates and actual values.

2 Write and solve an equation to show the change in Luisa's account using values rounded to the nearest $5 and nearest $1. _____

_____

3 What do the estimates tell you about whether Luisa has more or less money on Tuesday night than on Monday night? Do you think the amount of change is positive or negative? Explain. _____

_____

_____

4 Write and solve an equation to show the change in Luisa's account using exact values.

_____

5 Does this equation tell you whether Luisa has more or less money on Tuesday night than she did on Monday night? Explain. _____

_____

_____

6 Describe how solving the equation with estimates helped you solve the equation with exact values. _____

_____

_____

_____

Try It   Use what you just learned to solve these problems. Show your work on a separate sheet of paper.

7 Estimate $73.8 - (-9)$. Then solve. _____

8 Estimate $-17.7 \div 3$. Then solve. _____

Learn About **Estimating with Fractions**

Read the problem below. Then explore how estimating can be useful when computing with positive and negative fractions.

Jim stands on a dock that is $3\frac{3}{4}$ feet above the lake surface. He dives down $12\frac{1}{2}$ feet below the dock. What is Jim's vertical location relative to the lake surface? Show that your answer is reasonable.

▶ **Picture It** **You can use a number line to understand the problem.**

The number line models Jim's dive.

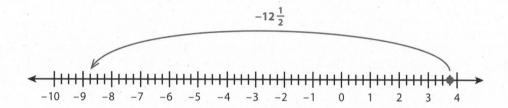

▶ **Model It** **You can also use rounding to help understand the problem.**

Round each mixed number to the nearest integer.

Actual Value	Nearest Integer
$3\frac{3}{4}$	4
$-12\frac{1}{2}$	-13

Connect It Now you will solve the problem from the previous page using estimates and actual values.

9 Write and solve an equation to show Jim's vertical location using values rounded to the nearest integer. _____

10 Based on your estimate, is Jim's position relative to the surface of the lake definitely positive, definitely negative, or too close to 0 to tell? Explain.

_____

_____

11 Write and solve an equation to show Jim's vertical location using exact values.

_____

_____

12 Describe how solving the equation with integers helped you solve the equation with exact values.

_____

_____

_____

_____

Try It Use what you just learned about estimating and computing with rational numbers to solve these problems. Show your work on a separate sheet of paper.

13 A sugar-water solution freezes at −1.8°C. A saltwater solution freezes at −13.6°C. What is the difference between the freezing temperature of the sugar-water solution and that of the saltwater solution? Estimate to show that your answer is reasonable.

_____

14 Cecilia records the weight change in her cat over 2 weeks. What number does she record as the total weight change for her cat?

My Cat's Weight Change			
Week	1	2	Total Change
Weight change (in pounds)	$-\dfrac{5}{16}$	$+\dfrac{3}{8}$	

_____

Practice ➤ **Solving Problems with Rational Numbers**

Study the example below. Then solve problems 15–17.

Example

Mr. Lee sets up a bank account to pay his rent. Each month a housing company deducts the same amount of rent from Mr. Lee's account. At the end of the year, the amount of money in Mr. Lee's account changed by −$8,328. Approximately how much does the amount in his account change in one month?

Look at how you could show your work using estimation.

Total change ÷ number of months = change per month

$$-8,328 \quad \div \quad 12 \quad = \quad ?$$

Use compatible numbers to estimate the answer.

Think: $84 \div 12 = 7$

−8,400 is close to −8,328.

$-8,400 \div 12 = -700$

Solution _−$700_____

> The student chooses numbers that are easy to divide and that are close to the actual numbers.

> 💬 **Pair/Share**
> Will the actual answer be greater or less than the estimate? How do you know?

15 Anita, Jared, and Steph are rock climbing. Anita is $42\frac{1}{2}$ feet below Jared. Steph is $67\frac{3}{4}$ feet above Anita. What is Steph's position compared to Jared? Estimate to show that your answer is reasonable.

Show your work.

> I think a simple diagram could help me understand the problem.

> 💬 **Pair/Share**
> Does your estimate tell you if the answer is definitely positive, definitely negative, or too close to 0 to tell?

Solution _____

16 Browning, Montana, holds the U.S. record for the greatest temperature drop in one day. On January 23, 1916, the temperature changed by an average of −4.17°F per hour. To the nearest degree, what was the total temperature change after 24 hours?

Show your work.

Was the total temperature change positive or negative?

Pair/Share

How does your estimate show that your answer is reasonable?

Solution _____

---

17 Fred is scuba diving. He stops 14.3 meters below the surface to look at a fish. Then he swims down 5.8 meters deeper to look at a reef. If he then swims up 3.2 meters, which is the BEST approximation of Fred's position relative to the ocean surface?

A 12 meters

B 11 meters

C −17 meters

D −23 meters

How will you decide if you should add or subtract each number?

Lena chose **B** as the correct answer. How did she get that answer?

_____

_____

_____

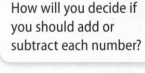**Pair/Share**

Does Lena's answer make sense?

Solving Problems with Rational Numbers

Solve the problems.

1 Which is the *best* estimate of $-\frac{15}{16} \div \left(-\frac{1}{2} \right)$?

A 2

B $\frac{1}{2}$

C 0

D -2

2 Which is the *best* estimate of $-\frac{15}{16} + \left(-\frac{1}{2} \right)$?

A $1\frac{1}{2}$

B $\frac{1}{2}$

C $-\frac{1}{2}$

D $-1\frac{1}{2}$

3 Beth plays a video game in which she starts with 0 points. In round 1, she loses $3\frac{1}{2}$ points; in round 2, she wins $28\frac{1}{2}$ points; and in round 3, she loses another $3\frac{1}{2}$ points. What is her final score?

A $-18\frac{1}{2}$

B $18\frac{1}{2}$

C $21\frac{1}{2}$

D $35\frac{1}{2}$

4 Ally, Barbara, and Katherine will share the cost of a vacation rental for a week. Ally agrees to pay 30% of the cost. Barbara agrees to pay 0.45 of the cost. Katherine will pay the remaining balance. If the total rental cost is $960, how much will Ally, Barbara, and Katherine each pay towards the week's rent?

Ally will pay $_____.

Barbara will pay $_____.

Katherine will pay $_____.

5 Given the six rational numbers below, come up with the greatest sum, difference, product, and quotient, using two of the numbers for each operation.

$$-5\frac{1}{2} \quad 3.75 \quad -20.8 \quad 8 \quad -4 \quad 11\frac{1}{4}$$

Greatest sum: _____ + _____ = _____

Greatest difference: _____ − _____ = _____

Greatest product: _____ × _____ = _____

Greatest quotient: _____ ÷ _____ = _____

6 A credit-card statement shows that Mrs. Gerardo owes between $35 and $45. Estimate to decide which of the items shown in the box might be on her statement. Then write an equation to justify your choices.

Show your work.

Payment	+30.00
Clothing Store	−21.75
Grocery Store	−26.25
Clothing Return	+12.36
Toy Store	−19.99
Mel's Diner	−7.35
Minimart	−5.17

Answer _____

✔ **Self Check** **Go back and see what you can check off on the Self Check on page 1.**

Solve the problems.

1 Which situation can be represented by the equation $-4 \times 5 = -20$?

A Jack exercised for 4 hours after school each day last week.

B The cost of a summer pool pass increased $4 each of the last 5 years.

C Amanda earned $4 for each of 5 classes in which she received an A.

D The temperature dropped 4 degrees each hour for 5 hours.

2 In which situation do the quantities combine to make 0?

A Emily ran 3 miles on Saturday and walked 3 miles on Sunday.

B Beverly bought a chair for $350 and sold it 3 years later for $350.

C Josh ran 2 laps counterclockwise around a track and then 2 laps clockwise around the track.

D Trey deposited $150 into his savings account on Friday and withdrew $100 the following week.

3 Which expression is equivalent to $19 - 27$?

A $27 - 19$

B $-(19 + 27)$

C $19 + (-27)$

D $-19 + 27$

4 Roger makes 70 gallons of pink paint by mixing 21 gallons of red paint with 49 gallons of white paint.

What part of every gallon is from

red paint? _____

The model represents one gallon of mixed paint.

Shade the correct number of bars to show how much of a gallon is from red paint.

5 The point on the number line shows the location of $-2\frac{1}{2}$. Write each expression in a box to show its correct location on the number line.

$$-2\frac{1}{2} + (-4) \qquad -2\frac{1}{2} - (-4)$$
$$-2\frac{1}{2} - 2\frac{1}{2} \qquad -2\frac{1}{2} + 2\frac{1}{2}$$

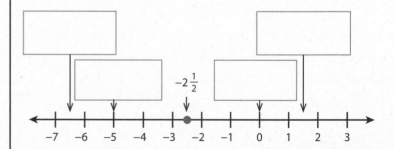

6 Fill in the boxes below with numbers that make the statements true.

$$\boxed{} + (-7.28) = \text{a positive number}$$

$$12 + \boxed{} = 0$$

$$\boxed{} - 2\frac{3}{4} = \text{a negative number}$$

$$-4.8 - \boxed{} = \text{a positive number}$$

$$-15 + 15 = \boxed{}$$

7 Nolan correctly spelled $\frac{13}{16}$ of his spelling words. How is $\frac{13}{16}$ written as a decimal?

Show your work.

Answer _____

Performance Task

Answer the questions and show all your work on separate paper.

Your rich uncle offers to buy you 100 shares of stock for your birthday. He gives you two companies to choose from. The table shows the daily closing price of one share of each company's stock for one week.

	Monday	Tuesday	Wednesday	Thursday	Friday
HooYa!	$29.50	$30.80	$28.90	$27.10	$27.50
FacePage	$26.30	$28.90	$25.10	$21.60	$24.00

Checklist

Did You . . .

☐ Organize and label all the information?

☐ Check all your calculations?

☐ Complete all parts of the problem?

a. Find the change in stock price from day to day for each company. Report each change as a positive or negative number.

b. Find the mean daily change in price for each company for this 5-day period. Describe the similarities and differences in the way each company's prices changed.

c. Decide which stock you will choose and explain your reasoning. If your uncle buys the stock at the closing price on Friday, how much will he pay for the 100 shares?

Reflect

Reflect on Mathematical Practices After you complete the task, choose one of the following questions to answer.

- **Persevere** What do a positive change and a negative change mean in the context of this problem?

- **Argue and Critique** What factors did you consider when making your choice of stock to buy?

Unit 2
Ratios and Proportional Relationships

Real-World Connection An article about the sports program at your school was in the paper today. It reports that the $150 per-sport fee that you pay will decrease by 30% next year. How much will you pay next year to play baseball? You are making muffins for this year's teacher appreciation breakfast. You need $\frac{3}{4}$ teaspoon of baking powder for a recipe that calls for 2 cups of flour. You'd like to increase the recipe to use 3 cups of flour, so how much baking powder will you need?

In This Unit You will learn how to use ratios to write proportions. You will also solve real-world problems involving proportions.

✓ Self Check

Before starting this unit, check off the skills you know below. As you complete each lesson, see how many more you can check off!

I can:	Before this unit	After this unit
find unit rates with complex fractions, for example: $\frac{1}{4}$ cup oats per $\frac{1}{2}$ cup flour = $\frac{1}{2}$ cup oats per 1 cup flour	☐	☐
identify proportional relationships and the constant of proportionality	☐	☐
graph proportional relationships	☐	☐
interpret a graph of a proportional relationship	☐	☐
solve multi-step percent problems involving tax, tips, markups, etc, for example: $5.00 + 5% tax = 5 × 1.05 = $5.25	☐	☐
solve multi-step percent problems involving percent change or percent error	☐	☐

Ratios Involving Complex Fractions

G Use What You Know

In Grade 6, you learned about unit rates. Take a look at this problem.

Jana is training for a triathlon that includes a 112-mile bike ride. Today, she rode her bike 12 miles in 45 minutes. What is Jana's rate in miles per hour?

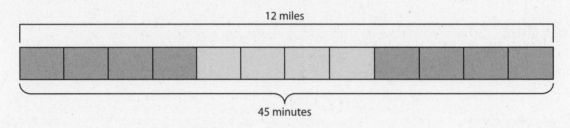

12 miles

45 minutes

Use the math you already know to solve the problem.

a. If Jana biked at a constant rate, how many miles did she bike in the first 15 minutes?

_____

b. At the same rate, how many miles did she bike in the next 15 minutes? _____

c. At the same rate, how many miles did she bike in the last 15 minutes? _____

d. How many more minutes would Jana need to bike to total one hour? _____

e. At the same rate, how many miles would she bike in that amount of time? _____

f. Explain how you could find the number of miles Jana bikes in one hour.

_____

_____

▷▷ Find Out More

The number of miles Jana bikes in one hour is a **unit rate**. A unit rate compares two quantities where the second quantity is 1. A unit rate tells you how many units of the first quantity correspond to one unit of the second quantity.

The units in this problem are miles and hours. The problem tells you that Jana bikes **12 miles** in **45 minutes**. That's the same as 12 miles in $\frac{3}{4}$ hour.

$$\frac{\text{number of miles}}{\text{number of hours}} = \frac{12}{\frac{3}{4}}$$

The fraction $\frac{12}{\frac{3}{4}}$ is a **complex fraction**. A complex fraction is a fraction where the numerator is a fraction, the denominator is a fraction, or both the numerator and the denominator are fractions. You can simplify a complex fraction by dividing, just as you would do if the numerator and denominator were whole numbers.

The fraction bar represents division, so you can think of $\frac{6 \text{ miles}}{2 \text{ hours}}$ as $6 \div 2 = 3$ miles per hour. You can think about $\frac{12 \text{ miles}}{\frac{3}{4} \text{ hour}}$ in the same way.

$$\frac{12}{\frac{3}{4}} = \frac{12}{1} \div \frac{3}{4}$$

$$= \frac{12}{1} \times \frac{4}{3}$$

$$= \frac{48}{3} \text{ or 16 miles per hour}$$

The unit rate is 16. The number of miles Jana bikes is 16 times the number of hours.

▷ Reflect

1 On another training ride, Jana bikes 15 miles in 50 minutes. Explain how you could find the number of miles she bikes in 1 hour.

_____

_____

_____

Learn About ▶ **Finding Unit Rates with Fractions**

Read the problem below. Then explore different ways to understand how to find a unit rate.

Max's favorite recipe for oatmeal raisin cookies makes 48 servings. He wants to make some cookies but only has one egg. Max has to adjust the amounts of the other ingredients. How much flour will he need?

RECIPE
OATMEAL RAISIN COOKIES

Ingredients

$\frac{3}{4}$ cup butter   1 teaspoon baking soda

2 eggs $\frac{3}{4}$ teaspoon cinnamon

$1\frac{1}{2}$ cups flour $2\frac{3}{4}$ cups oats

$1\frac{1}{2}$ cups brown sugar   1 cup raisins

1 teaspoon vanilla

▶ **Model It** **You can draw a double number line to show the relationship described in the problem.**

The units you need to compare are cups of flour and eggs.

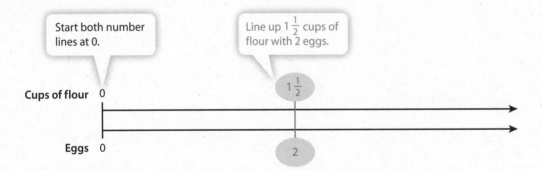

Start both number lines at 0.

Line up $1\frac{1}{2}$ cups of flour with 2 eggs.

You need to find the unit rate, the number of cups of flour needed for **1** egg.

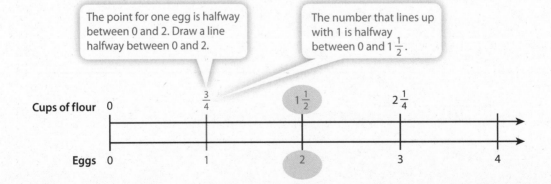

The point for one egg is halfway between 0 and 2. Draw a line halfway between 0 and 2.

The number that lines up with 1 is halfway between 0 and $1\frac{1}{2}$.

Connect It Now you will see how to solve the problem from the previous page by writing a ratio.

2 Why do you need to find the number that is halfway between 0 and $1\frac{1}{2}$?

_____

3 How could you find the number that is between 0 and $1\frac{1}{2}$?

_____

4 How many cups of flour does Max need to use if he has just 1 egg? Show your work.

_____

5 Write the ratio that compares $1\frac{1}{2}$ cups of flour to 2 eggs.

$$\frac{\text{cups of flour}}{\text{eggs}} = \underline{\qquad}$$

6 Write and simplify a division expression to find the number of cups of flour Max needs to use if he has just 1 egg.

_____

_____

7 The unit rate is _____. The number of cups of flour is _____ times the number of eggs.

8 Explain how to find a unit rate. _____

_____

_____

Try It Use what you just learned about finding a unit rate to solve these problems. Show your work on a separate sheet of paper.

Use the information in the recipe on the previous page.

9 If Max has only one egg, how much butter will he need? _____

10 If Max has only one cup of flour, how much vanilla will he need? _____

Learn About ⟩ **Comparing Unit Rates**

Read the problem below. Then explore different ways to understand how to find and compare unit rates.

> José's mother is trying to decide whether or not she should buy a 12-ounce package of coffee on sale for $7.50. She knows that she can buy the same coffee for $9.00 per pound. Which is the better buy?

▶ **Model It** **You can draw a double number line to show the relationship described in the problem.**

To find the better buy, compare the unit rate of each option.

The problem gives you one unit rate: $9.00 per pound. To compare unit rates, the units you use must be the same. So, find the weight of the other coffee in pounds.

There are 16 ounces in 1 pound, so 12 ounces is $\frac{12}{16}$ or $\frac{3}{4}$ pound.

You can write $7.50 using fractions. $7.50 is the same as $7\frac{1}{2}$.

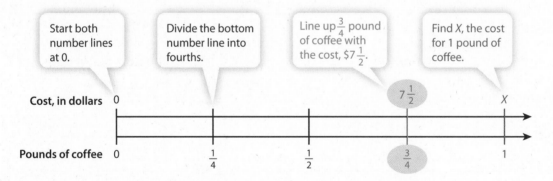

Start both number lines at 0.

Divide the bottom number line into fourths.

Line up $\frac{3}{4}$ pound of coffee with the cost, $7\frac{1}{2}$.

Find *X*, the cost for 1 pound of coffee.

Find the **cost for each quarter-pound of coffee**. Then find the **unit cost**.

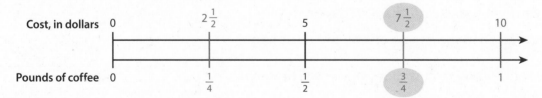

Connect It Now you will see how to use a ratio to solve the problem.

11 The top number line is divided into 3 equal parts from 0 to $7\frac{1}{2}$, and the bottom number

line is divided into 3 equal parts from 0 to $\frac{3}{4}$. How can you use this to find the cost of

1 pound of coffee? _____

_____

_____

12 Write the ratio that compares $\$7\frac{1}{2}$ dollars to $\frac{3}{4}$ pound of coffee. $\dfrac{\text{dollars}}{\text{pounds of coffee}} =$ _____

13 Write and simplify a division expression to find the cost of 1 pound of coffee.

_____

14 Which is the better buy, 12 ounces for $7.50 or 1 pound for $9.00? Explain your reasoning.

_____

_____

_____

15 If you started the problem by converting 1 pound to 16 ounces, would you get the same

result? Justify your conclusion. _____

_____

16 Can you compare any two unit rates? Explain. _____

_____

Try It Use what you just learned about unit rates to solve this problem. Show your work on a separate sheet of paper.

17 Rina's recipe uses 2 cups of sugar to make $2\frac{1}{2}$ dozen cookies. Jonah's recipe uses

$2\frac{1}{4}$ cups of sugar to make 3 dozen cookies. Which recipe uses more sugar for a dozen

cookies? Why? _____

_____

Practice ▷ **Finding Ratios Involving Complex Fractions**

Study the example below. Then solve problems 18–20.

Example

Oliver is training for a marathon. In practice, he runs 15 kilometers in 72 minutes. What is his speed in kilometers per hour?

Convert the time in minutes to hours to find kilometers per hour.

72 minutes = 1 hour 12 minutes

$$= 1\frac{12}{60} \text{ hours or } 1\frac{1}{5} \text{ hours}$$

$$\frac{km}{hr} = \frac{15}{1\frac{1}{5}}$$

$$= 15 \div 1\frac{1}{5}$$

$$= 15 \div \frac{6}{5}$$

$$= 15 \times \frac{5}{6}$$

$$= \frac{75}{6} \text{ or } 12\frac{1}{2}$$

Solution _____

> The student knew that 60 minutes = 1 hour, so 72 minutes = 60 minutes + 12 minutes, or 1 hour 12 minutes.

> 💬 **Pair/Share**
> How did you decide how to write the ratio?

---

18 Alexis washes $10\frac{1}{2}$ windows in $\frac{3}{4}$ hour. At this rate, how many windows can she wash in one hour?

> How do you evaluate a complex fraction?

> 💬 **Pair/Share**
> How can you tell if your answer is reasonable?

Solution _____

19 A restaurant uses $8\frac{1}{4}$ pounds of carrots to make 6 carrot cakes. Frank wants to use the same recipe. How many pounds of carrots does Frank need to make one carrot cake?

Show your work.

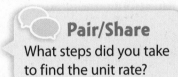
What is the ratio of pounds of carrots to cakes?

Solution _____

_____

Pair/Share
What steps did you take to find the unit rate?

---

20 It takes Zach 15 minutes to walk $7\frac{1}{2}$ blocks to the swimming pool. At this rate, how many blocks can he walk in one minute? Circle the letter of the correct answer.

A $\frac{1}{5}$ block

B $\frac{1}{2}$ block

C 2 blocks

D 5 blocks

What unit rate do you need to find?

Dee chose **C** as the correct answer. What was her error?

_____

_____

_____

_____

Pair/Share
Does Dee's answer make sense?

Practice > Finding Ratios Involving Complex Fractions

Solve the problems.

1 One of the highest snowfall rates ever recorded was in Silver Lake, Colorado, in April 1921, when just over 7 feet of snow fell in $27\frac{1}{2}$ hours. What was that rate in inches per hour?

A $\frac{14}{55}$ inch per hour

C $3\frac{3}{55}$ inches per hour

B $\frac{55}{158}$ inch per hour

D $3\frac{13}{14}$ inches per hour

2 A grocery store sells different types of Trail Mix, as shown in the table below.

	Trail Mix A	Trail Mix B	Trail Mix C
Cost ($)	6	8.50	2.25
Weight	$\frac{3}{4}$ lb	1 lb	4 oz

1 lb = 16 oz

Which statement is correct?

A Trail Mix A is the best buy.

C Trail Mix C is the best buy.

B Trail Mix B is the best buy.

D They are all the same price.

3 A treadmill counts $\frac{1}{5}$ mile as one lap. The display of the treadmill indicates the number of laps already completed and highlights how much of the current lap has been completed. Create a display that shows a total of $\frac{13}{10}$ miles run.

• Write one number in the box to indicate the number of laps already completed.

• Shade in one or more sections of the display to indicate how much of the current lap has been completed.

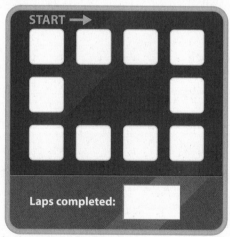

Total distance run: $\frac{13}{10}$ miles

4 A restaurant makes a special citrus dressing for its salads. Here is how the ingredients are mixed:

$\frac{1}{3}$ of the mixture is oil $\frac{1}{4}$ of the mixture is orange juice

$\frac{1}{6}$ of the mixture is vinegar $\frac{1}{4}$ of the mixture is lemon juice

When the ingredients are mixed in the same ratio as shown above, every batch of dressing tastes the same. Study the measurements for each batch in the table. Fill in the blanks so that every batch will taste the same.

	Batch 1	Batch 2	Batch 3
Oil (cups)	1		
Vinegar (cups)		1	
Orange juice (cups)	$\frac{3}{4}$		1
Lemon juice (cups)			1

5 Two friends worked out on treadmills at the gym.

- Alden walked 2 miles in $\frac{3}{4}$ hour.

- Kira walked $1\frac{3}{4}$ miles in 30 minutes.

Who walked at a faster rate? Explain your reasoning.

Show your work.

Answer _____

_____

✓ Self Check   Go back and see what you can check off on the Self Check on page 77.

Understand Proportional Relationships

Think It Through

What is a proportional relationship?

Suppose you and some friends plan to go to a movie and the tickets cost $8 each.

You will pay $8 for 1 ticket, $16 for 2 tickets, $24 for 3 tickets, $32 for 4 tickets, and so on. The ratios of the total cost of the tickets to the number of tickets are all equivalent.

A group of ratios that are equivalent are in a **proportional relationship**. When ratios are equivalent, they all have the same unit rate. In a proportional relationship, the unit rate is called the **constant of proportionality**.

Think **How can you use a table to tell if a relationship is proportional?**

The table below shows the total cost of movie tickets based on the number of tickets you buy.

Total Cost of Tickets ($)	8	16	24	32
Number of Tickets	1	2	3	4

> **Circle** the ratio in the table that shows the constant of proportionality.

The ratios of the total cost of tickets to the number of tickets are equivalent. The ratios all simplify to $\frac{8}{1}$ or 8, so **the ratios are in a proportional relationship**.

$$\frac{8}{1} = 8 \qquad \frac{16}{2} = 8 \qquad \frac{24}{3} = 8 \qquad \frac{32}{4} = 8$$

The unit rate is 8, so the constant of proportionality is 8. The equation $c = 8t$, where c is the total cost and t is the number of tickets, represents this relationship. The total cost is always 8 times the number of tickets.

The table below shows the cost to play in the town soccer tournament.

Total Cost ($)	7	8	9	10
Number of Family Members	1	2	3	4

You can find and simplify the ratios of the total cost to the number of family members.

$$\frac{7}{1} = 7 \qquad \frac{8}{2} = 4 \qquad \frac{9}{3} = 3 \qquad \frac{10}{4} = 2\frac{1}{2}$$

The ratios are not equivalent, so **the quantities are not in a proportional relationship**.

Think How can you use a graph to tell if a relationship is proportional?

You can use a graph to determine if a relationship is proportional.

The data for the cost of movie tickets and the cost to participate in the soccer tournament can be modeled by the graphs below.

> Compare the two graphs. How are they alike? How are they different?

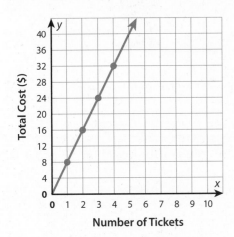

Number of Tickets

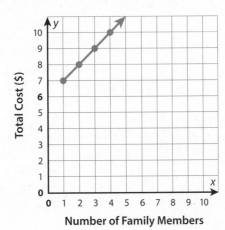

Number of Family Members

The points on the graphs are on a straight line for both sets of data, but only the data for the cost of movie tickets goes through the origin. This means that only the total cost of the movie tickets compared to the number of tickets is a proportional relationship.

Proportional Relationship	Non-Proportional Relationship
• The graph can be represented by a **straight line**. • The straight line **goes through the origin**.	• The graph may or may not be represented by a straight line. • If the graph is a straight line, it does not go through the origin.

▶ Reflect

1 Look at the graph that compares the total cost to the number of movie tickets you buy. How can you use the graph to find the cost of 5 movie tickets?

_____

_____

_____

Think About **Identifying Proportional Relationships**

Let's Explore the Idea Use the table below to analyze the cost of downloading applications to a phone.

Number of Downloads	2	4	5	6	10
Total Cost ($)	6	12	15	18	30

2 How can you find the ratio of the total cost to the number of downloads?

_____

3 What is the ratio of the total cost to the number of downloads when you download

2 applications? _____ 4 applications? _____ 5 applications? _____

6 applications? _____ 10 applications? _____

4 Are the data in the table in a proportional relationship? If so, what is the constant

of proportionality? _____

_____

Now try these problems.

5 The table shows the number of hours needed for different numbers of people to clean up after a school dance.

Hours Needed to Clean Up	12	9	8	6
Number of People Cleaning	2	3	4	6

Are the quantities in the table in a proportional relationship? Explain your reasoning.

_____

6 The students in the Service Club are mixing paint to make a mural. The table below shows the different parts of paint that the students mix together.

	A	B	C	D	E
Parts of Red Paint	1	2	4	2	3
Parts of White Paint	3	4	8	6	9

Two mixtures of paint will be the same shade if the red paint and the white paint are in the same ratio. How many different shades of paint did the students make? Explain.

Let's Talk About It
Solve the problems below as a group.

7 Refer to the situation in Problem 6. Which shades of paint are the most red? Why?

_____

_____

_____

8 Use the table in Problem 6. Plot a point for each ordered pair. After you plot each point, draw a line connecting the point to (0, 0).

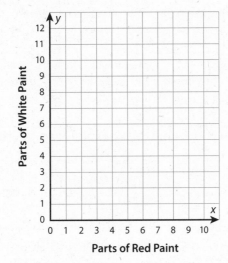

9 Based on the graph, what do the mixtures that are the same shade have in common? What does this tell you about their relationship?

_____

_____

▶ Try It Another Way   Work with your group to determine whether the equation represents a proportional relationship. Explain your choice. You may want to make a table similar to those in Problems 5 and 6 or a graph similar to that in problem 8 on separate sheet of paper to support your reasoning.

10 $y = 2x + 4$ _____

11 $y = 2x$ _____

Connect **Identifying Proportional Relationships**

Talk through these problems as a class. Then write your answers below.

12 Compare The graphs below show the number of points you earn in each level of a game. Which games, if any, have a proportional relationship between the number of points you earn and the level of the game? In which game can you earn the most points in Level 2? Explain your answer.

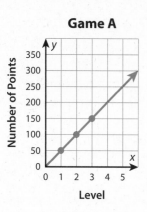

Game A

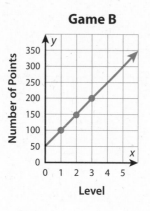

Game B

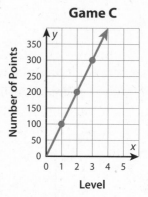

Game C

_____

_____

_____

13 Apply Servers at a snack shop use the table below to find the total cost for frozen yogurt, but some of the numbers have worn off. The total cost is proportional to the number of cups of frozen yogurt. Find the missing numbers in the table.

Number of Cups of Frozen Yogurt	1	2	3	4
Total Cost ($)				18.00

14 Analyze Michael says that the difference between Dani's and Raj's ages is always the same, so Raj's age is proportional to Dani's age. Is Michael correct? Explain.

	2010	2015	2020	2025
Dani's Age	5	10	15	20
Raj's Age	10	15	20	25

_____

_____

Identifying Proportional Relationships   93

15 **Put It Together** Use what you know to complete this task.

> Paige works in an art store that sells square pieces of canvas. There are 5 different squares to choose from.
>
> | Canvas | A | B | C | D | E |
> |---|---|---|---|---|---|
> | **Length of side (in feet)** | 1 | 2 | 3 | 4 | 5 |

Part A Make a table to show the perimeter for each square piece of canvas. Use the formula $P = 4s$. Then draw a graph to compare the length of a side of each square to its perimeter. Use your table and graph to explain whether this is a proportional relationship.

Part B Make a table to show the area for each square piece of canvas. Use the equation $A = s^2$. Then draw a graph to compare the length of a side of each square to its area. Use your table and graph to explain whether this is a proportional relationship.

Equations for Proportional Relationships

Use What You Know

In Lesson 10, you learned about proportional relationships and how they are represented on a graph. In this lesson you will learn about equations that represent proportional relationships.

The table shows how the number of people who can ride a rollercoaster depends on the number of cars on the rollercoaster.

Number of Cars	Number of People
3	18
5	30
6	36
8	48

How many people can ride in 1 car? In 10 cars?

Use the math you already know to solve the problem.

a. Find the ratio of the number of people to the number of rollercoaster cars for each set of data in the table.

_____

b. Are the ratios of the number of people to the number of rollercoaster cars in a proportional relationship? Explain your reasoning.

_____

c. How many people can ride in 1 car? _____

d. What is the constant of proportionality for the data in the table? _____

e. Explain how you can find the number of people that can ride in a rollercoaster with 10 cars.

_____

f. Write an equation to represent the number of people, y, that can ride the rollercoaster with x cars. _____

The problem on the previous page is shown using a table. You can also represent this situation with both a graph and an equation. In each representation, you can identify the constant of proportionality.

The graph represents the problem on the previous page.

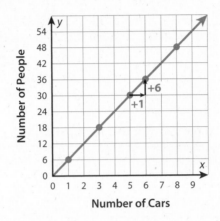

The **constant of proportionality** is **the unit rate**, or **the value of y when x = 1**, which is 6. In the graph, the value of y increases by 6 each time the value of x increases by 1.

The equation $y = 6x$, where y is the number of people who can ride the rollercoaster and x is the number of cars on the rollercoaster, represents this situation. Just as with the graph, the constant of proportionality is the value of y when $x = 1$.

If two quantities, x and y, are in a proportional relationship, then **the ratio** $\frac{y}{x}$ equals the constant of proportionality. This means that you can represent any proportional relationship with the following equation:

$y =$ **constant of proportionality** $\cdot x$

Reflect

1 Explain how the constant of proportionality is represented in the table, the equation, and the graph of the rollercoaster situation.

_____

_____

_____

_____

_____

Learn About **Writing Equations for Proportional Relationships**

Read the problem below. Then explore ways to represent a proportional relationship.

Jesse is making punch. For every 3 cups of juice, he needs 6 cups of seltzer. Represent this proportional relationship using a table, a graph, and an equation and identify the constant of proportionality. What does the constant of proportionality represent in this situation?

▶ **Model It** **You can use a table to represent the relationship.**

The ratio of seltzer to juice will be the same for all quantities.

All ratios will be equivalent to $\frac{6}{3} = \frac{2}{1}$.

Seltzer	2	3	4	5	6	7	8
Juice	1	1.5	2	2.5	3	3.5	4

▶ **Model It** **You can use a graph to represent the relationship.**

Graph the point (3, 6) and connect it to the point (0, 0). Identify points on the line.

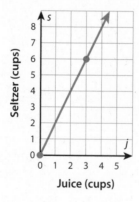

▶ **Model It** **You can use an equation to represent the relationship.**

The ratio of seltzer to juice is $\frac{6}{3} = \frac{2}{1}$. This means that for every 1 cup of juice, you need 2 cups of seltzer.

amount of seltzer = constant of proportionality • amount of juice

Connect It Now you will solve the problem from the previous page.

2 In the table on the previous page, what does the ratio $\frac{2}{1}$ represent in terms of

the problem? _____

_____

3 What does the point (2, 4) represent on the graph? _____

_____

4 Which point on the graph can be used to find the constant of proportionality?

_____

_____

5 Use the constant of proportionality to write an equation to represent s, the number of

cups of seltzer you need for j cups of juice. _____

6 Use the equation you wrote in problem 5 to find the amount of seltzer you need if you

have 15 cups of juice. _____

7 For a different punch recipe, the equation $s = 4c$ represents the number of cups of
seltzer, s, that you need for c cups of cranberry juice. What is the constant of

proportionality? Explain. _____

_____

_____

Try It Use what you just learned to solve these problems. Show your work on a separate sheet of paper.

8 Kelsey can buy 2 pounds of apples for $7. Write an equation to represent the cost, c, for

a pounds of apples. _____

9 The equation $m = 32 \cdot g$ represents the average number of miles, m, that a car can go on
g gallons of gas. What is the constant of proportionality and what does it represent in

this situation? _____

_____

Practice ▶ **Writing Equations for Proportional Relationships**

Study the example below. Then solve problems 10–12.

Example

Julie is making bracelets. The table shows the number of bracelets she can make with different lengths of cord. Determine if the relationship is proportional. If so, find the constant of proportionality and write an equation to represent the situation.

Number of Bracelets (b)	Yards of Cord (c)
12	3
18	$4\frac{1}{2}$
24	6
30	$7\frac{1}{2}$

Show your work.

The student simplifies the ratios using the rules of division.

Possible student work:

$\frac{3}{12} = \frac{1}{4}$ $\frac{6}{24} = \frac{1}{4}$

$\frac{4\frac{1}{2}}{18} = \frac{\frac{9}{2}}{18} = \frac{9}{2} \div 18 = \frac{9}{2} \times \frac{1}{18} = \frac{1}{4}$ $\frac{7\frac{1}{2}}{30} = \frac{\frac{15}{2}}{30} = \frac{15}{2} \times \frac{1}{30} = \frac{1}{4}$

Solution $c = \frac{1}{4}b$; The constant of proportionality is $\frac{1}{4}$.

Pair/Share
How do you know that the relationship is proportional?

---

10 Michael reads 12 pages of a book in 18 minutes, 8 pages in 12 minutes, and 20 pages in 30 minutes. Is this a proportional relationship? If so, what is the constant of proportionality? What does it represent? Write an equation to represent this situation.

Show your work.

How can you find the constant of proportionality?

Solution _____

_____

_____

Pair/Share
Describe other ways you can find the constant of proportionality.

11 The equation $c = 2.5t$ represents the cost, c, for t tickets to the school play. Does a value of 3.5 for t make sense in this situation? Explain your reasoning.

Show your work.

What does t represent?

Solution _____

_____

_____

Pair/Share
Describe a situation in which the equation $y = 2.5x$ can have values for x that are mixed numbers.

---

12 The graph shows the height, h, in inches, of a plant after d days. The plant had a height of 4 inches after 6 days. Which equation can you use to represent the situation?

A $h = 4d$

B $h = 6d$

C $h = \frac{3}{2}d$

D $h = \frac{2}{3}d$

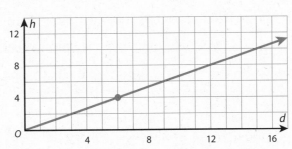

What point on the graph represents the constant of proportionality?

Stephen chose **C** as his answer. Explain his error.

_____

_____

_____

_____

Pair/Share
How do you know that the graph shows a proportional relationship?

Lesson 11 Equations for Proportional Relationships   **99**

Practice ▶ Writing Equations for Proportional Relationships

Solve the problems.

1 The equation $r = \frac{3}{4}b$ represents the number of cups of raisins, r, that you need to make b batches of trail mix. Which point would be on a graph that represents this proportional relationship?

A $\left(\frac{3}{4}, 1\right)$　　　　**C** (3, 4)

B (4, 3)　　　　　　**D** $\left(0, \frac{3}{4}\right)$

2 Look at the graph. What is the meaning of the point shown with a star?

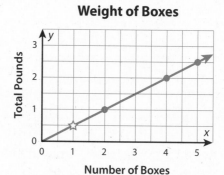

Weight of Boxes

A Half of a box weighs 1 pound.

B Each box weighs $\frac{1}{2}$ pound.

C Each box weighs 1 pound.

D Each box weighs 2 pounds.

3 A baker is making dough for bread. The number of cups of flour he uses is proportional to the number of loaves he makes. The baker uses $18\frac{3}{4}$ cups of flour to make 5 loaves of bread. Which of the following correctly represents this proportional relationship? Select all that apply.

A $f = 3\frac{3}{4}b$, where f is the number of cups of flour and b is the number of bread loaves.

D

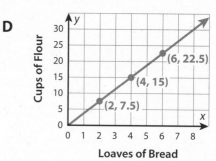

B

Cups of flour	$23\frac{3}{4}$	$28\frac{3}{4}$	$33\frac{3}{4}$
Number of loaves	10	15	20

C $b = 3\frac{3}{4}f$, where f is the number of cups of flour and b is the number of bread loaves.

4 The graph shows the total amount of dog food that Sophia's dog Nipper eats. Which statement is NOT correct?

A The data represents a proportional relationship.

B The point (5, 2) means that Nipper eats 5 pounds of dog food in 2 days.

C The point (0, 0) has no meaning in this situation.

D The constant of proportionality is 0.4.

Amount of Dog Food Eaten

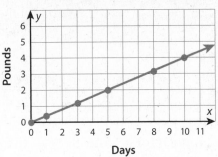

5 Len wants to paint a wall in his house. He knows that 1 can of paint covers an area of 32 square feet. The dimensions of the wall are shown. Shade in the correct number of paint cans he will need to buy.

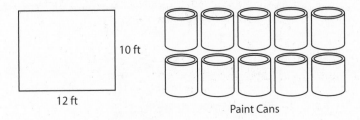

10 ft

12 ft

Paint Cans

6 Tom and Jeff studied the data in the table. They each wrote an equation to represent the relationship between the number of students and the number of pizzas ordered.

Tom's equation: $p = \frac{1}{4}s$

Jeff's equation: $s = 4p$

The teacher said that both equations were correct. Explain why.

Students (s)	Pizzas (p)
28	7
12	3
32	8
16	4

_____

_____

_____

_____

✓ **Self Check**   **Go back and see what you can check off on the Self Check on page 77.**

Problem Solving with Proportional Relationships

Ⓖ Use What You Know

You have learned how to recognize and represent proportional relationships. Now you can apply this understanding to solve problems with percents. Take a look at this problem.

It's the end of the soccer season and all equipment at the Sports Stop is on sale. What is the sale price of a soccer ball that regularly sells for $28?

THE SPORTS STOP

All soccer equipment is on sale for **20% OFF** the regular price!

END OF SEASON SALE

Use the math you already know to help understand the problem.

a. What does "20% off the regular price" mean?

_____

b. How do you write 20% as a decimal? _____

c. What is the regular price of the soccer ball? _____

d. How would you find 20% of the regular price? What would you do with this amount to find the sale price?

_____

_____

e. What is the sale price? _____

f. Summarize the steps you would take to find the sale price given the regular price and a percent discount.

_____

_____

You can use a bar model to represent the problem from the previous page. The model helps you to see the relationship between the parts and the whole. The sale price and the amount of the discount make up the regular price.

Regular Price $28.00	
Sale Price s	Discount 20% of $28.00

You can write an equation to represent this relationship where s = sale price.

$$s = 28 - (20\% \text{ of } 28)$$

Percents are used in many different real-world situations. Here are some other types of real-world situations involving percent that you will work with in this lesson.

markup: a percent added to the cost of an item to determine the selling price

simple interest: a percent of an amount borrowed that is paid to the lender in addition to the amount borrowed

tax: a percent of a purchase that is added to the purchase and paid to a government

gratuity: a percent added on to the cost of a service, for example a tip given to a waiter

commission: a percent of a sales amount awarded to the person making the sales

► Reflect

1 In the bar model above, the discount is 20%. What percent of the regular price is the sale price? Explain how you could solve the problem using this information.

_____

_____

_____

_____

_____

Learn About **Proportional Relationships with Simple Interest**

Read the problem below. Then explore different ways to understand how to solve problems involving simple interest.

> Joshua borrows $300 from his older sister to buy a bike. He promises to pay the total amount plus 5% simple interest in one year. How much will Joshua pay back in all?

▶ **Picture It** **You can use a bar diagram to show the relationship between the amount borrowed, the interest, and the amount that must be paid back.**

The diagram shows that the amount borrowed plus the amount of simple interest paid equals the total amount to pay back. The percentage is the interest rate.

Total Amount to Pay Back (t)	
Amount Borrowed $300	Simple Interest 5% of $300 for 1 year

▶ **Model It** **You can write an equation to help find the total amount to pay back including the interest paid each year.**

You can write the equation in words and then fill in the numbers you know. Write the percent as a decimal.

Amount Borrowed	+	Amount of Interest in 1 year	=	Total Amount to Pay Back
300	+	0.05×300	=	t

Connect It Now you will solve the problem from the previous page using an equation.

2 Look at the bar diagram. What term refers to the amount Joshua has to pay back in addition to the $300 he borrows? _____

3 What is the interest rate in the bar diagram? _____ How is the interest rate expressed in the equation? _____

4 Look at the equation. What does 0.05 × 300 represent?

_____

What does each number in the expression 0.05 × 300 represent?

_____

5 Show how to find how much interest Joshua pays in one year. _____

6 Show how to find the total amount Joshua has to pay back in one year including interest.

_____

7 Describe how to find the total amount to pay on a loan when paying simple interest.

_____

_____

Try It Use what you just learned about simple interest to solve these problems. Show your work on a separate sheet of paper.

8 Morgan's mom wants to borrow $720 to buy a new computer. The store will charge her 8% simple interest for one year. How much will she have to pay back if she pays the full amount in one year?

_____

9 A bank advertises that they will pay 1.5% simple annual interest on new savings accounts. Lorenzo puts $400 in a new account. If he does not deposit or withdraw any money, how much will he have altogether after one year?

_____

Learn About ▶ **Problem Solving with Percents**

Read the problem below. Then explore different ways to find the regular price of an item given the discount rate and sale price.

> Nia told Patrick that her new backpack only cost $14 because she used a 30% off coupon when she bought it. Patrick wants to buy a similar backpack. How much will it cost if he does not have a 30% off coupon?

▶ **Picture It** You can use a tape diagram to represent the sale price and regular price of the item.

You know that percents represent parts of a whole. In this problem, the regular price is the whole, and the discount and discounted price represent the parts.

With the coupon, the discounted price of the backpack is 30% off the regular price. Since 30% + 70% is 100%, the price Nia paid for the backpack is 70% of the regular price.

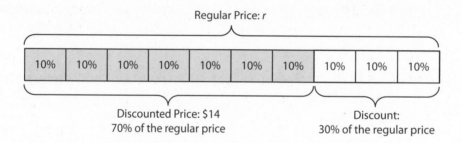

Regular Price: r

| 10% | 10% | 10% | 10% | 10% | 10% | 10% | 10% | 10% | 10% |

Discounted Price: $14
70% of the regular price

Discount:
30% of the regular price

▶ **Model It** You can also use an equation to model the problem.

The discounted price is 30% off the regular price.

The regular price is 100%.
Because 100% − 30% = 70%, the discounted price is 70% of the regular price.

regular price (100%) − discount (30%)   The problem gives this price.

(100% − 30%) of the regular price = discounted price

70% of regular price (r) = $14

$0.70r = 14$

Connect It Now you will solve the problem from the previous page using the diagram and equation.

10 Look at the tape diagram in *Picture It*. How many sections are used to show the discounted price? _____

11 If the discounted price is $14, how much money does one section represent?

_____

12 If all ten sections show the original price, explain how to find the regular price.

_____

13 Now look at the equation in *Model It*. What do 0.70, 14, and r represent?

_____

_____

14 Show how to solve the equation to answer the question in the problem.

_____

_____

15 Suppose a sale price is $18 and the discount is 25%. Explain how to find the regular price.

_____

Try It Use what you just learned about percents, parts, and wholes to solve these problems. Show your work on a separate sheet of paper.

16 Deanna gets 3 problems incorrect on a math quiz. Her score is 85%. How many questions are on the quiz?

_____

17 A store owner buys backpacks at a certain price and sells them at a higher price. The difference is called the markup. If she pays $21 for a backpack and adds a 40% markup on the price she paid, what is the selling price?

_____

Practice ▸ Problem Solving with Proportional Relationships

Study the example below. Then solve problems 18–20.

Example

Samuel pays $31.50 for a jacket. The amount includes 5% sales tax. How much is the jacket without sales tax?

Look at how you can show your work using a diagram.

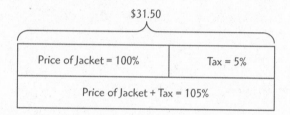

$31.50

| Price of Jacket = 100% | Tax = 5% |
| Price of Jacket + Tax = 105% | |

105% = 1.05

Let p = the price of the jacket without tax.

$1.05p = 31.50$

$p = 30$

Solution _The price of the jacket is $30._

> **The student decided to use the price of the jacket without tax as 100% or 1. This is a quick way to find a price with tax.**

> **Pair/Share**
> How could you solve the problem using the price of the jacket with tax as 100%?

---

18 Tony sells sporting goods. He makes a 10% commission on every dollar of sales that he makes. One month Tony got a commission check for $2,500. What were his sales in dollars that month?

Show your work.

> **Make sure you read the problem carefully and identify what the given numbers represent in the equation you write.**

> **Pair/Share**
> If Tony wants to earn $3,200 in commissions for a month, what would his sales amount have to be?

Solution _____

19 The regular price for a pair of shoes is $48. The store is having a buy one get one $\frac{1}{2}$ off sale. If you buy 2 pairs of shoes for that price, what percent discount is that?

Show your work.

How can you write $\frac{1}{2}$ off as a percent?

 Pair/Share
Show how to solve the problem in a different way.

Solution _____

---

20 A store spends $10 for each pair of Brand X jeans and adds a 120% markup to the cost. What is the selling price of the jeans? Circle the letter of the correct answer.

A $11.20

B $12.00

C $22.00

D $130

Phil chose **B** as the correct answer. How did he get that answer?

_____

_____

_____

Remember, 120% means $\frac{120}{100}$. How do you write this as a decimal?

 Pair/Share
Suppose the markup is 150%. What would the selling price be?

Practice ▷ **Problem Solving with Proportional Relationships**

Solve the problems.

1 Which expression CANNOT be used to calculate the total amount paid for a meal (*m*) including a 15% tip?

A $m + 0.15m$

B $m + 1.15m$

C $m + \dfrac{3}{20}m$

D $1.15m$

2 Elena gets a base pay of $1,500 per month. She also earns a commission of 8% of the total sales dollars that she makes. What are Elena's earnings for a month in which she has sales of $32,000?

A $1,620

B $2,560

C $4,060

D $27,100

3 Jack is a car salesman who works strictly on commission. For every car he sells, he earns a 2% commission. Cars sell for $35,000 each. Shade in the number of cars Jack needs to sell in order to reach his target income of $5,000 for the end of the month?

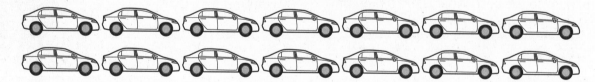

4 Joshua does not want to spend more than $22 on a long-sleeved shirt. Which description of shirt prices would keep Joshua within his spending limit, not including tax? Select all that apply.

   A 15% off $25

   B 30% off $32

   C $19.65 plus a $2.35 shipping fee

   D $20.45 plus a $1.60 shipping fee

5 The Outdoor Furniture Center buys wooden benches for $50 each. The furniture store owner adds a 200% markup to the cost of the bench. After hearing from customers that the selling cost of the bench is too high, the owner changes the markup to 120%. How much less per bench does the store owner make with the lower markup?

Show your work.

Answer The owner makes _____ less per bench using the lower markup.

6 The owner of the Outdoor Furniture Center decides to use the 120% markup. At the end of the season, he wants to sell all the benches that are in stock. He sells the benches for 20% off. What is the total price of a bench with this discount plus a 5% sales tax?

Show your work.

Answer The total price of a bench with the discount and tax is _____.

 **Self Check** **Go back and see what you can check off on the Self Check on page 77.**

Lesson 13 👥 Introduction
Proportional Relationships

↻ Use What You Know

In Lesson 12 you learned about solving problems involving percents. In this lesson, you will solve percent problems that involve increases and decreases. Take a look at this problem.

> In May, Susana earned $40 from pet-sitting. In June, her earnings increase 200%. How much does she earn in June?

Use the math you already know to help understand the problem.

a. First consider 100%. What is 100% of $40? _____

b. How does 200% compare to 100%?

_____

c. How much is 200% of $40? Explain how you know.

_____

d. How much is 200% more than $40? _____

e. How much did Susana earn in June? _____

f. Explain what it means when a value increases by 100%, and what it means when a value increases by 200%.

_____

_____

_____

▷▷ Find Out More

When a quantity changes over time, it is often useful to compare the original quantity and the new quantity by describing the difference, or amount of change, as a **percent**. The **percent change** is the ratio that compares the amount of the change to the original amount.

$$\frac{\text{amount of change}}{\text{original amount}} = \text{percent change}$$

The percent change will be a **percent increase** when the new amount is greater than the original amount. The percent change will be a **percent decrease** when the new amount is less than the original amount. You can use a ratio to find Susana's June earnings.

$$\frac{x}{40} = 200\%$$

$$\frac{x}{40} = \frac{200}{100}$$

$$\frac{x}{40} = 2$$

$$x = 80$$

In June, Susana earned **$40 + $80**, or $120.

Percent error is the ratio describing how far an estimate is from the actual amount.

$$\frac{\text{amount of error}}{\text{actual amount}} = \text{percent error}$$

For example, if you estimate that your book is 11 inches long but it is really 10.875 inches long, the percent error is $\frac{0.125}{10.875}$ or about 1.1%.

▷ Reflect

1 How is a percent error like a percent change?

_____

_____

_____

Learn About ▶ **Finding Percent Change**

Read the problem below. Then explore different ways to find the percent change.

Nassim scored 5 goals in his first soccer season and 8 goals in his second soccer season. What was the percent increase in the number of goals he scored?

▶ **Picture It** **You can use a bar model to compare the change to the original amount.**

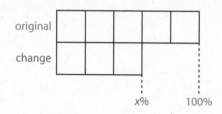

Once you know the amount of increase, you can find the percent increase.

▶ **Model It** **You can use a proportion to compare the change to the original amount.**

$$\frac{\text{amount of change}}{\text{original amount}} = \text{percent change}$$

$$\frac{8-5}{5} = \frac{x}{100}$$

$$\frac{3}{5} = \frac{x}{100}$$

▶ **Connect It** **Now you will solve the problem from the previous page and a new, similar problem.**

2 Solve the proportion in *Model It* on the previous page. By what percent did the number of goals Nassim scored increase?

_____

3 Explain the relationship between the *x* in the proportion and the *x* in the bar model and

tell what each *x* represents. _____

_____

4 Nassim scored 12 goals in his third soccer season. Write and solve a proportion to show the percent increase in the number of goals scored from the first season to

the third season. _____

_____

5 What does it mean to have a percent increase of more than 100%?

_____

6 Explain why it makes sense for the original amount to be the denominator when you

write a proportion to find the percent change. _____

_____

_____

_____

▶ **Try It** **Use what you just learned to solve these problems. Show your work on a separate sheet of paper.**

7 Amelia's mom baked 48 cookies. After Amelia and her friends walk through the kitchen, there are 18 cookies left. What is the percent decrease in the number of cookies?

_____

8 The first month Tan had his new phone, he downloaded 5 apps on it. Six months later, he has 22 apps on his phone. What is the percent increase in the number of apps Tan has on his phone?

_____

Lesson 13 Proportional Relationships   **115**

Learn About **Finding Percent Error**

Read the problem below. Then explore different ways to understand it.

Leo estimates that a package weighs 24 pounds. The postal clerk weighs it and finds it weighs 20 pounds. What is the percent error in Leo's estimate?

▶ **Picture It** **You can use a bar model to help understand the problem.**

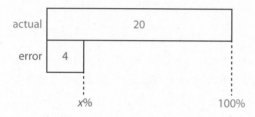

▶ **Model It** **You can use a proportion to help understand the problem.**

$$\frac{\text{amount of error}}{\text{actual amount}} = \frac{x}{100}$$

$$\frac{24 - 20}{20} = \frac{x}{100}$$

$$\frac{4}{20} = \frac{x}{100}$$

Connect It Now you will solve the problem from the previous page and a new, similar problem.

9 Solve the proportion in *Model It* on the previous page. What was the percent error in Leo's estimate?

_____

10 Explain the relationship between the *x* in the proportion and the *x* in the bar model and tell what each *x* represents.

_____

_____

11 Leo estimated the weight of another package to be 20 pounds but the weight was actually 24 pounds. Write and solve a proportion to show this percent error. Write your answer to the nearest whole percent.

_____

12 Both of Leo's estimates were off by 4 pounds. Explain why the percent error was different for the two estimates even though the difference was the same.

_____

_____

Try It Use what you just learned to solve these problems. Show your work on a separate sheet of paper.

13 Emma needs 84 centimeters of ribbon. She measures and cuts a piece from a spool of ribbon. Later she finds out she has actually cut 80 centimeters of ribbon. What is her percent error? Write your answer to the nearest whole percent.

_____

14 Christopher estimates it will take him half an hour to complete his math homework. He is able to complete it in 25 minutes. What is the percent error in his estimate?

_____

Practice Finding Percent Change and Percent Error

Study the example below. Then solve problems 15–17.

Example

When Juan got his puppy, she weighed 8 pounds. Now that she is 1 year old, her weight is 60 pounds. What is the percent increase in the puppy's weight?

Look at how you could write a proportion that will help you solve the problem.

$$\frac{\text{amount of change}}{\text{original weight}} = \frac{x}{100}$$

$$\frac{52}{8} = \frac{x}{100}$$

$$6.5 = \frac{x}{100}$$

$$100 \cdot 6.5 = \frac{x}{100} \cdot 100$$

$$650 = x$$

Solution ___The puppy's weight increased by 650%.___

> Remember that the original amount, not the new amount, is the denominator.

💬 **Pair/Share**
What does it mean when an increase is greater than 100%?

---

15 The tennis team is selling tickets to a car wash for $6. When they do not sell very many tickets, the team decreases the price 25%. What is the new cost of a ticket?

Show your work.

> If the percent decrease is 25%, how do you find the amount of decrease?

💬 **Pair/Share**
By what fraction did the team decrease the price of the tickets?

Solution _____

16 Irene thinks she has space for a 45-inch-wide bookcase. It turns out that she only has space for a 40-inch-wide bookcase. What is the percent error in Irene's measurement?

Show your work.

What is the ratio of the amount of error to the actual width?

Solution _____

Pair/Share

If Irene thinks she has space for a 35-inch-wide bookcase, will the percent error be the same?

17 On Thursday, 30 students went to after-school tutoring. On Friday, 6 students went. What is the percent decrease in the number of students who went to tutoring? Circle the letter of the correct answer.

A 20%

B 80%

C 400%

D 500%

What number do you use in the denominator of the ratio?

Brittany chose **A** as the correct answer. How did she get this answer?

_____

_____

_____

Pair/Share

Why can't a percent decrease be greater than 100%?

Practice **Finding Percent Change and Percent Error**

Solve the problems.

1 Mr. Krogman usually prices the umbrellas in his store at $8 each. However, on rainy days he increases the price by 75%. How much does he charge for an umbrella on a rainy day?

   A $2

   B $6

   C $9.38

   D $14

2 Last year 80 students signed up for a summer trip to Washington, D.C. This summer 50 students have signed up to go. What is the percent decrease in the number of students?

   A 30%

   B 37.5%

   C 60%

   D 62.5%

3 Jerold's weekly pay rate is $865. He receives a 25% pay raise. How can Jerold calculate his new weekly pay rate? Select all that apply.

   A divide $865 by 0.25

   B divide $865 by 1.25

   C multiply $865 by 0.25

   D multiply $865 by 1.25

   E Solve for x: $\dfrac{x}{865} = \dfrac{125}{100}$

   F Solve for x: $\dfrac{865}{x} = \dfrac{25}{100}$

4 A student conducted an experiment on plant growth. Plant A was fed a different fertilizer than Plant B. Before the experiment began, Plant A measured 14 centimeters tall, and Plant B measured 16 centimeters tall. At the end of the experiment, Plant A measured 18.2 centimeters tall, and Plant B measured 20 centimeters tall. Which plant, A or B, grew at a greater rate?

Plant _____ grew at a greater rate.

5 Diana guesses that there are 120 gum balls in a jar. There are actually 96. In another game she guesses that there are 75 jelly beans in a jar. There were actually 60. In which game did Diana have the smallest percent error?

Show your work.

Answer _____

6 In the spring, the owner of a sporting goods store decreases the price of winter gloves from $10.00 to $8.00. She increases the price of swimming goggles from $8.00 to $10.00. Without doing the math, do you think that the percent decrease in the price of gloves is the same as the percent increase of the goggles? Explain why or why not.

Answer _____

_____

Now use math to show whether or not the percent decrease and percent increase are the same. Explain why or why not.

Show your work.

Answer _____

_____

✓ **Self Check** **Go back and see what you can check off on the Self Check on page 77.**

Solve the problems.

1 Paul is making banana bread. The number of cups of bananas he uses is proportional to the number of loaves of bread. Paul uses $11\frac{1}{4}$ cups of bananas to make 5 loaves of bread. Which equation represents the relationship between c, the number of cups of bananas, and b, the number of loaves of bread?

A $c = \frac{4}{9}b$

B $c = 2b$

C $c = 2\frac{1}{4}b$

D $c = 5b$

2 Henry sells apples. The graph shows the relationship between the price of apples and their total weight.

What does the point (0, 0) on the graph mean?

A Henry didn't sell any apples last week.

B Henry does not make any money for selling apples.

C Henry didn't make any money last week selling apples.

D Henry does not make money if he sells no apples.

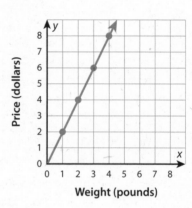

Weight (pounds)

3 Kelly hiked in the woods. It took her $\frac{1}{14}$ hour to walk $\frac{1}{4}$ mile. After she snacked, she walked another $\frac{1}{6}$ mile in $\frac{1}{16}$ hour. Choose *True* or *False* for each statement.

a. Before her snack, Kelly walked at a rate of $\frac{4}{14}$ miles per hour. ☐ True ☐ False

b. For the second part of her hike, Kelly walked at a rate of $2\frac{2}{3}$ miles per hour. ☐ True ☐ False

c. It took Kelly 2 hours longer to walk $\frac{1}{6}$ mile than it did for her to walk $\frac{1}{4}$ mile. ☐ True ☐ False

d. Kelly walked over 30% faster before her snack than she did after her snack. ☐ True ☐ False

4 Traci wants to buy rings that cost $50 each. A jeweler is offering a deal in which you buy 1 ring and get the 2nd for 25% off and the 3rd for 50% off. The sales tax is 8%. Traci will buy 3 rings. How much money will Traci save using the deal instead of paying full price for all 3 rings?

Traci will save $ _____

5 The graph shows the relationship between the number of hours Angie works and the amount of money she earns.

Is there a proportional relationship between the number of hours Angie works and the amount of money she earns? Explain. If there is a proportional relationship, what is the constant of proportionality?

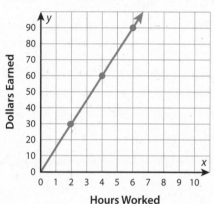

Dollars Earned
Hours Worked

ITs a straight line and it starts at the origin, the constant of proportion relationship is $15 a hour

6 Coach Shaw is buying baseball equipment for his team. He gets a reduced rate if he buys 8 baseballs for every 3 batting helmets. The reduced rate is $2.25 per baseball and $22.50 per helmet. The sales tax on each item is 6%. Coach Shaw has $400 in his budget to buy baseballs and helmets. What is the *greatest* number of baseballs and helmets he can buy at the reduced rate if the ratio of baseballs to helmets is 8:3?

Show your work.

Answer _____

Performance Task

Answer the questions and show all your work on separate paper.

In three weeks, Raj's favorite store is having a sale on jeans. All jeans will be 50% off the regular price. Raj also has a coupon that will give him 30% off his total purchase. "Yay, 80% off!" he exclaims. He wants to buy one pair of jeans that is regularly $50, one pair that is regularly $30, and one pair that is regularly $20.

Raj calculated how much money, to the nearest dollar, he will need for his jeans and plans to save the same amount each of the next three weeks until he has enough for the jeans. His calculations are shown below.

Regular price total: $50 + $30 + $20 = $100

I will pay 100% − 80% = 20% of the price.

Total price after the discount = $100 × 0.20
                                = $20

Raj thinks he needs to save about $7 each week to have enough money in 3 weeks' time.

Raj made a mistake when calculating how much money he will need to buy the jeans. Describe his mistake. Then, figure out how much he will need for the jeans and decide on a new savings plan. About how much will Raj need to save each week to be able to afford his jeans?

Checklist

Did You . . .

☐ Identify the mistake Raj made?

☐ Correctly solve the problem to find how much Raj needs to save?

☐ Figure out Raj's new savings plan?

▶ Reflect

Reflect on Mathematical Practices After you complete the task, choose one of the following questions to answer.

- **Argue and Critique** How did you discover and explain Raj's mistake?

- **Reason Mathematically** How do you know that your answer makes sense?

Unit 3
Expressions and Equations

Real-World Connection Toby asked his mom whether they should take the Greenway Path or the Rocky Road for their Saturday hike. His mom said, "Six of one, half a dozen of the other." His mom was trying to say that the paths were just about the same, so it didn't matter which one they hiked. In mathematics you often look for expressions that are the same, or equivalent. Calculating the price of a pair of sneakers advertised as "20% off" is the same as figuring out that the sale price is 80% of the original cost. Reporting that a fifth of your class took part in the 7th-grade play is the same as saying 20% of your class took part.

In This Unit You will find equivalent expressions and write linear expressions. You will also solve problems using equations and inequalities.

✔ Self Check

Before starting this unit, check off the skills you know below. As you complete each lesson, see how many more you can check off!

I can:	Before this unit	After this unit
find equivalent linear expressions, for example: $1.2x + 1.3x + 0.2y + 0.1y = 2.5x + 0.3y$	☐	☐
rewrite linear expressions in different ways, for example: $x + 0.2x = 1.2x$	☐	☐
solve problems with equations	☐	☐
solve problems with inequalities	☐	☐

Equivalent Linear Expressions

Use What You Know

In previous years you learned how to write expressions in many different ways. Take a look at this problem.

> Micah and three friends bought a total of 4 bags of pretzels and 4 drinks at the snack stand. If a bag of pretzels costs *x* dollars, and a drink costs *y* dollars, what expression could you write to show how much the friends spent in all?

Use the math you already know to solve the problem.

a. Suppose each friend bought 1 bag of pretzels and 1 drink. Write an expression to show how much they spent in all.

_____

b. Suppose instead that one friend bought all 4 bags of pretzels and another friend bought all 4 drinks. Write an expression that shows the total cost.

_____

c. Suppose one friend decided to pay for a bag of pretzels and a drink for all 4 of them. What expression could you write to show the total cost?

_____

d. Explain how the first two expressions are related.

_____

_____

e. Explain how the last two expressions are related.

_____

_____

_____

Expressions that have the same value are **equivalent** expressions. Numerical expressions such as $8 + 2$, $15 - 5$, $40 \div 4$, and 2×5 are all equivalent. They are all equal to 10.

Take a look at the following algebraic expressions. They are all equivalent.

Expression 1: $(x + y) + (x + y) + (x + y) + (x + y)$

Expression 2: $4x + 4y$

Expression 3: $4(x + y)$

To show that Expression 1 is equal to Expression 2, you can use the commutative and associate properties of addition to group and change the order of the terms.

$(x + y) + (x + y) + (x + y) + (x + y) = (x + x + x + x) + (y + y + y + y) = \mathbf{4x + 4y}$

To show that Expression 2 is equal to Expression 3, you can use the distributive property to factor 4 from both terms of the expression.

$\mathbf{4x + 4y = 4(x + y)}$

You can also evaluate these expressions to see if they are equivalent. If you know that a bag of pretzels costs $2 and a drink costs $3, you can substitute 2 for x and 3 for y into each of the three expressions above.

$(x + y) + (x + y) + (x + y) + (x + y) = (2 + 3) + (2 + 3) + (2 + 3) + (2 + 3) = \mathbf{20}$

$4x + 4y = 4(2) + 4(3) = 8 + 12 = \mathbf{20}$

$4(x + y) = 4(2 + 3) = 4(5) = \mathbf{20}$

The expressions all have a value of **20**.

▶ Reflect

1 Write two other expressions equivalent to $4x + 4y$. Explain your thinking.

_____

_____

_____

Read the problem below. Then explore different ways to write equivalent expressions for the perimeter of a square.

> The length of a side of a square is $c - 9$. Three students wrote three different expressions for the perimeter of this square. Are the expressions equivalent? Explain why or why not.

▶ **Model It** **Miguel wrote the perimeter as the sum of the four equal side lengths.**

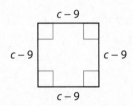

Perimeter $= (c - 9) + (c - 9) + (c - 9) + (c - 9)$

▶ **Model It** **Jessica rearranged the terms, putting the like terms together.**

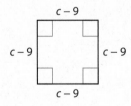

Perimeter $= c + c + c + c - 9 - 9 - 9 - 9$

▶ **Model It** **Petria multiplied the number of sides by the length of a side.**

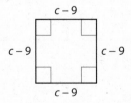

Perimeter $= 4(c - 9)$

Connect It Now you will use properties of operations to decide whether or not all the expressions are equivalent.

2 Look at Miguel's expression and Jessica's expression. What is the same and what is different about them?

_____

_____

3 Simplify Miguel's expression. _____ Simplify Jessica's expression. _____

Are the expressions equivalent? _____

4 Use the distributive property to rewrite Petria's expression. _____

Is Petria's expression equivalent to the other two? _____

5 Can you think of another way to show that all three expressions are equivalent?

_____

_____

6 How can you use properties of operations to decide whether or not expressions

are equivalent? _____

_____

_____

Try It Use what you just learned about equivalent expressions to solve these problems. Show your work on a separate sheet of paper.

7 The perimeter of a square is given as $12x + 20$. Write two different expressions to represent its perimeter. Use factoring for one way.

_____

_____

8 Write two different expressions equivalent to $8d - 4$. Use factoring for one way.

_____

_____

Learn About **Finding Equivalent Expressions**

Read the problem below. Then explore whether or not the expressions are equivalent.

Ms. Lim asked her class to find an expression equivalent to $7 - 3(4 - 2x) - 10x$.

One step in each of the following students' work is incorrect. Find and explain the error. Then write your own expression equivalent to the one given above.

▶ **Solve It**

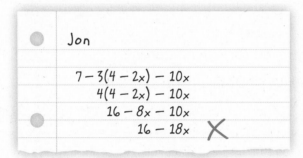

Jon

$7 - 3(4 - 2x) - 10x$
$4(4 - 2x) - 10x$
$16 - 8x - 10x$
$16 - 18x$ ✗

▶ **Solve It**

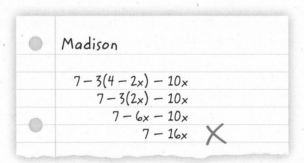

Madison

$7 - 3(4 - 2x) - 10x$
$7 - 3(2x) - 10x$
$7 - 6x - 10x$
$7 - 16x$ ✗

▶ **Solve It**

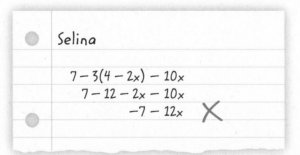

Selina

$7 - 3(4 - 2x) - 10x$
$7 - 12 - 2x - 10x$
$-7 - 12x$ ✗

Connect It Now you will think about properties and the order of operations to solve the problem.

9 Jon didn't follow the order of operations. Explain what he did wrong.

_____

10 Madison made a mistake when she combined terms. Explain what Madison did wrong.

_____

11 Selina didn't use the distributive property correctly. Where did she go wrong? Explain your thinking. _____

_____

12 Write an expression that is equivalent to $7 - 3(4 - 2x) - 10x$. Show your work.

_____

_____

_____

13 How can you be sure you've used the properties of operations correctly to form an expression that is equivalent to the original one?

_____

_____

Try It Use what you just learned about equivalent expressions to solve these problems. Show your work on a separate sheet of paper.

14 Is $-8 - 2(3 + 2n) + 7n$ equivalent to $-30 - 13n$? Explain why or why not.

_____

_____

15 Is $-\frac{1}{4}y + 2\frac{1}{4}y + 2 - y$ equivalent to $y + 2$? Explain why or why not.

_____

_____

Practice > **Finding Equivalent Linear Expressions**

Study the example below. Then solve problems 16–18.

Example

The length of a rectangle is three times its width, *w*. Write three different expressions to describe its perimeter.

Use what you know about rectangles and perimeter to draw a diagram.

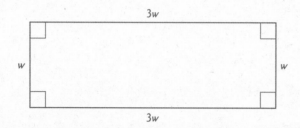

Expression 1:
$3w + w + 3w + w$, the sum of all 4 sides

Expression 2:
$2(3w) + 2(w)$, the sum of twice the length and twice the width

Expression 3:
$2(3w + w)$, twice the sum of the length and the width

Solution $3w + w + 3w + w; 2(3w) + 2(w); 2(3w + w)$

The student drew a diagram to help write expressions for the perimeter.

> **Pair/Share**
> How could you use the distributive property to write one of the expressions for the perimeter?

---

16 The expression $12c - 18$ represents the perimeter of a regular hexagon. Write two different expressions to describe its perimeter. Then write an expression for the length of one of its sides.

Show your work.

The sides of a regular polygon are all the same length.

Solution _____

_____

_____

> **Pair/Share**
> How might drawing a diagram help you solve the problem?

17 Is $\frac{1}{4}(8y - 12)$ equivalent to $2y - 12$? Explain why or why not.

Show your work.

I know that the distributive property works the same for fractions as for whole numbers.

Solution _____

_____

_____

_____

Pair/Share

What is another way to tell whether or not two expressions are equivalent?

---

18 Which expression below is equivalent to $-3x + 5(x + 2)$? Circle the correct answer.

A $2x + 2$

B $-x + 2$

C $2x + 10$

D $-8x + 10$

Kaitlin chose **A** as the correct answer. How did she get that answer?

_____

_____

_____

Which operation must I perform first in this problem?

Pair/Share

How would you help Kaitlin understand her error?

Practice ▶ **Finding Equivalent Linear Expressions**

Solve the problems.

1 Which of the following expressions is equivalent to $-\frac{1}{4}y - 2\frac{1}{4}y + \frac{1}{2}(4 - 2y)$?

A $-3y + 2$

B $-3\frac{1}{2}y + 2$

C $-4y + 4$

D $-4\frac{1}{2}y + 2$

2 In the following equation, c and d are both integers.

$$4cx - 5c = -12x + d$$

What is the value of c? _____

What is the value of d? _____

3 Consider the equation below.

$$5(3a - 1) - 2(3a + 2) = 3(a + 2) + v$$

Select two expressions that are equivalent to v.

A $-a - 10$

B $3(5a + 2)$

C $6a - 7$

D $3(2a - 5)$

E $6a - 15$

F $3(a + 2)$

G $6(a - 15)$

H $-6a - 4$

4 The length of a side of an equilateral triangle is $x - 4.5$. First express its perimeter as a sum. Next express its perimeter as a product. Explain why the two expressions are equivalent.

_____

_____

_____

_____

_____

5 The length of each of the two congruent sides of an isosceles triangle is $2n + 7$ and the length of the third side is $3n$. Draw and label the triangle. Then write two equivalent expressions for its length of the perimeter.

Show your work.

_____

_____

_____

✓ **Self Check** **Go back and see what you can check off on the Self Check on page 125.**

🔄 Use What You Know

You've learned how different expressions can represent the same situation. Take a look at this problem.

This swimming pool was designed so that sections of the pool can be used for different activities. The dimensions are given in meters. Write three different expressions to represent the total surface area of the pool.

lap swimmers	water therapy	8
swim lessons	kids' area	x
25	7	

Use the math you already know to solve the problem.

a. You can think about the total surface area of the pool as the sum of the surface areas of the swimming sections and the other sections. Write an expression that represents this way of thinking about the total surface area.

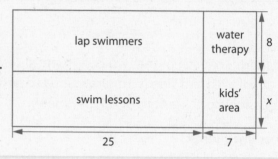

area of swimmers sections + area of other sections

$8 + x$

25

$8 + x$

7

_____

b. You can think about the total surface area as $25(8) + 7(8) + 25x + 7x$. Draw and label a picture that shows this way of thinking about the total surface area.

c. You can think about the total surface area as $(25 + 7)(8 + x)$. Explain the thinking behind this expression.

_____

_____

▷▷ Find Out More

The expressions that you wrote to represent the surface area of the pool are **equivalent expressions**. Each expression shows a different way of looking at the situation.

You can use properties of operations to show that expressions are equivalent. Another way to test whether two or more expressions are equivalent is to evaluate them for specific values of the variable. For example, you could evaluate each expression for $x = 10$.

$$25(8 + x) + 7(8 + x) = 25(8 + 10) + 7(8 + 10)$$
$$= 25(18) + 7(18)$$
$$= 450 + 126$$
$$= 576$$

$$25(8) + 7(8) + 25x + 7x = 25(8) + 7(8) + 25(10) + 7(10)$$
$$= 200 + 56 + 250 + 70$$
$$= 576$$

$$(25 + 7)(8 + x) = (25 + 7)(8 + 10)$$
$$= 32(18)$$
$$= 576$$

No matter which expression you use to find the total surface area of the pool, you get **576 square meters** as your answer. The three expressions are equivalent. If you choose a different value for x, the three expressions will have a different value, but they will all be equal.

▶ Reflect

1 If you know the value of x, which expression would you use to find the total surface area of the pool? Explain.

_____

_____

_____

_____

_____

Read the problem below. Then explore different ways to write an expression to solve the problem.

> A group of rectangular community gardens is being built on an empty city block. The length of each garden will be 90 feet, but the widths of the gardens will vary. Let g stand for the width of a garden. Think about different ways to find the perimeter of each garden. Then write an expression to represent each different way.

▶ **Picture It** **You can think about the perimeter of the rectangle as the sum of its sides.**

You can think about walking around the rectangle. The sum of its sides equals:

$$90 + g + 90 + g$$

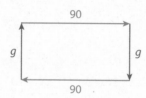

▶ **Picture It** **You can think about the perimeter of the rectangle as the sum of twice its length and twice its width.**

If you see the perimeter as the sum of two equal lengths and two equal widths, you can multiply the length by 2 and the width by 2 and then add the products.

$$2(90) + 2g$$

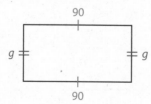

Connect It Now you will write the perimeter in a third way and show that all the expressions are equivalent.

2 Look at the diagrams on the previous page. Find the lengths of two adjacent sides. Write an expression for the sum of two adjacent sides. _____

3 The other pair of adjacent sides has the same sum. Explain how you could think of the perimeter of the rectangular garden as a product of the sum of two sides.

_____

4 Write an expression for the perimeter of the rectangular garden as a product of the sum of two sides. _____

5 Now use all three ways to show how to find the perimeter of a rectangular garden that is 16 feet long and 5 feet wide.

_____

6 Does it matter which expression you use to find the perimeter? Explain.

_____

_____

Try It Use what you just learned to solve these problems. Show your work on a separate sheet of paper.

7 Students in Jay's school plant vegetables in one of the rectangular gardens with length 90 feet and width $7\frac{1}{2}$ feet. Use each of the expressions above to find the garden's perimeter. Show that all three expressions produce the same measurement.

_____

_____

_____

8 Write the following expression in two different ways: $\frac{1}{2}(a + b)$.

_____

Learn About ▶ Writing Equivalent Expressions with Percents

Read the problem below. Then explore how to write different expressions to represent and solve it.

> The original price of a backpack is $40.90. The sale price is 30% off. Write two different expressions to represent its sale price.

▶ **Picture It** **You can draw a bar diagram to represent the situation.**

The whole bar represents the original price of the backpack.

The shaded section represents the 30% discount.

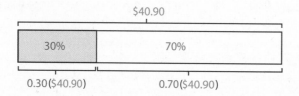

▶ **Model It** **You can calculate the sale price by subtracting the 30% discount from the original price.**

sale price = **original price − discount**

sale price = **original price − 30%** of **the original price**

= **40.90 − 0.30** (40.90)

▶ **Model It** **You can calculate the sale price by finding 70% of original price.**

sale price = **70%** of **the original price**

= **0.70** (40.90)

Connect It Now you will show that both expressions give you the same sale price.

9 Explain how you could find the sale price of the backpack using two operations.

_____

_____

10 Calculate the sale price of the backpack using two operations. Show your work.

_____

_____

11 Explain how you could find the sale price of the backpack using one operation.

_____

_____

12 Calculate the sale price of the backpack using one operation. Show your work.

_____

_____

13 Suppose the price of the backpack was p dollars. Write two different expressions to represent the sale price.

_____

_____

Try It Use what you just learned to solve these problems. Show your work on a separate sheet of paper.

14 The price of a flash drive that regularly sells for $16 is increased by 15%. Write two different expressions to find the new price.

_____

15 The original price of a DVD is represented by the variable x. If the DVD is discounted 45%, write a subtraction expression and a multiplication expression to represent its sale price.

_____

Practice Writing Equivalent Expressions

Study the example below. Then solve problems 16–18.

Example

A store manager paid $15 for a computer case and sells it in the store for 65% more than she paid. What expression represents the price of the computer case in the store?

Look at one way you could write an expression.

original price + 65% of original price = sale price

$$\downarrow \qquad \downarrow \qquad \downarrow \qquad\qquad \downarrow$$

$$15 \quad + \quad 0.65 \quad \cdot \quad 15 \qquad = \text{sale price}$$

Solution ___15 + 0.65(15)___

The student wrote an expression by finding the increase and adding it to the original cost.

 Pair/Share
What is another way to write an expression to represent the sale price?

---

16 A hand-woven rectangular rug measures x ft long and $2\frac{4}{5}$ ft wide. Write an expression to represent the perimeter of the rug.

Show your work.

What do I know about a rectangle that will help me solve this problem?

 Pair/Share
How many different ways can you represent the perimeter of the rug?

Solution _____

17 A customer calculated the cost of a new jacket, *c*, including a 7% sales tax, by multiplying 0.07 times the cost of the jacket and adding the product to the cost of the jacket. What is another way to calculate the price including tax? What expression represents the total cost?

Show your work.

I know that sales tax is added to the original cost of the jacket to find the total cost.

Solution _____

Pair/Share
Which method would you use to solve the problem?

18 The price of a $198.00 smart phone is discounted 40% for a special promotion. What is its sale price during the promotion? Circle the correct answer.

A $190.08

B $120.80

C $118.80

D $79.20

Will the sale price be more or less than $198.00?

Courtney chose **D** as the correct answer. How did she get that answer?

_____

_____

_____

_____

Pair/Share
How could you explain to Courtney the way to find the correct answer?

Practice ▶ **Writing Equivalent Expressions**

Solve the problems.

1 Jonathan and Trina both earn $12 per hour, but Trina earned a $15 bonus this week for being on time every day. Let J = number of hours that Jonathan worked this week and T = number of hours that Trina worked this week. Which expression represents the total amount that Jonathan and Trina earned this week?

A $12(J + T + 15)$

B $12(J + 15) + 12(T + 15)$

C $15(J + T) + 12$

D $12(J + T) + 15$

2 For expressions a–e, select *Yes* or *No* to indicate whether each expression is equivalent to $3(x + 2)$.

a. $3x + 2$ ☐ Yes ☐ No

b. $3(2 + x)$ ☐ Yes ☐ No

c. $3x + 2x$ ☐ Yes ☐ No

d. $x + 2x + 2 + 4$ ☐ Yes ☐ No

e. $x + x + x + 1 + 1 + 1 + 1 + 1 + 1$ ☐ Yes ☐ No

3 A store is advertising a sale with 15% off all prices in the store. Sales tax is 8%. Which equation will correctly determine the total cost, C, of buying an item with an original price of p, after the discount and sales tax are included? Select all that apply.

A $C = 1.08p - 0.15p$

B $C = 1.15p + 0.08p$

C $C = 1.08(0.85p)$

D $C = 0.85p + (0.08)0.85p$

E $C = p - 0.15p + 0.08p$

4 The length of a rectangle is x feet. Its width is $(x - 7)$ feet. Draw and label a rectangle to represent this situation. Then write three different expressions you could use to find its perimeter.

Show your work.

Answer _____

5 The perimeter of an equilateral triangle is $6x - 6.3$. Draw and label a triangle to represent this situation. Then write an expression to represent its perimeter as a sum. Then write an expression to represent its perimeter as a product.

Show your work.

Answer _____

_____

✓ **Self Check** **Go back and see what you can check off on the Self Check on page 125.**

🔄 Use What You Know

You know how to compute with rational numbers and write and solve one-step equations. Take a look at this problem.

Mr. Lombardo took his two children to a water park. He used the coupon shown below to buy one adult ticket. The price of admission for all three family members was $76. What was the price of each child's ticket?

WORLD OF
WATER

This coupon is good
for one adult ticket
to World of Water
at a price of $28.00.

YOU
SAVE
$4.00!

Use the math you already know to solve the problem.

a. What ticket price do you know? How much is that ticket? Explain.

_____

b. What other information is given in the problem?

_____

c. How can you find the price of the two children's tickets? Show how to find the answer.

_____

_____

d. If you know the price of two children's tickets, how can you find the price of one child's ticket?

_____

e. What is the price for each child's ticket? Show your work.

_____

You can also solve the problem from the previous page by writing and solving an equation. You know that the price of the adult ticket plus the price of two children's tickets is $76.

price of adult ticket	+	number of children	·	price of child's ticket	=	total cost
$28	+	2	·	p	=	$76

You can write this as $28 + 2p = 76$. This equation includes two operations, so it is a two-step equation.

Solve the equation for p, and compare to the operations used in the arithmetic solution on the previous page.

$28 + 2p = 76$ $28 - 28 + 2p = 76 - 28$ $2p = 48$	Using arithmetic, the first operation was to subtract the price of the adult ticket from the total cost. In the equation, **subtract 28** from both sides and simplify.
$2p \div 2 = 48 \div 2$ $p = 24$	The second operation was to **divide** the price for two tickets ($48) **by 2** to find the price for 1 ticket. In the equation, divide both sides by 2 and simplify.

To solve an equation, you perform operations so that the variable ends up alone on one side. Remember, the expressions on opposite sides of the equal sign are equivalent. If you perform an operation that changes the value of the expression on one side, you need to perform the same operation on the other side.

▶ Reflect

1 Explain the steps you could use to solve $3y + 6 = 30$ to find y.

_____

_____

_____

_____

Learn About Solving Two-Step Problems with Fractions

Read the problem below. Then explore different ways to solve two-step problems that involve fractions.

> Marvin made some candles that each weighed $\frac{3}{4}$ pound. He shipped them in a box that weighed 3 pounds. The total weight of the box filled with candles was 12 pounds. How many candles did Marvin ship in the box?

▶ **Model It** You can use arithmetic to solve a two-step problem that involves fractions.

Total weight of box and candles: 12 lb

Weight of box: 3 lb

Weight of all candles: 12 lb − 3 lb = 9 lb

Weight of all candles ÷ weight of one candle: $9 \div \frac{3}{4} = 9 \cdot \frac{4}{3}$, or 12

There are 12 candles in the box.

▶ **Model It** You can write an equation to solve a two-step problem that involves fractions.

Let $c =$ the number of candles that Marvin shipped in the box.

weight of 1 candle		number of candles	+	weight of box	=	total weight
$\frac{3}{4}$	·	c	+	3	=	12

To find the value of c, get c by itself on one side of the equation.

$$\frac{3}{4}c + 3 = 12$$

$$\frac{3}{4}c + 3 - 3 = 12 - 3$$

$$\frac{3}{4}c = 9$$

$$\frac{3}{4}c \cdot \frac{4}{3} = 9 \cdot \frac{4}{3}$$

$$c = 12$$

Connect It Now you will analyze the solution from the previous page.

2 What is the first operation performed in the arithmetic solution and in solving the equation? _____

3 How does the first operation get you closer to isolating *c* on one side of the equation?

_____

_____

4 Why do you multiply both sides by $\frac{4}{3}$ next?

_____

5 What does multiplying 9 by $\frac{4}{3}$ represent in the arithmetic solution?

_____

_____

6 Explain how to solve an equation that includes a variable with a coefficient added to a constant.

_____

_____

Try It Use what you just learned to solve these problems. Show your work on a separate sheet of paper.

7 Solve the equation. Show all steps in the solution.

$$\frac{2}{3}x + 1 = 5$$

_____

8 The formula to convert degrees Celsius to degrees Fahrenheit is $\frac{9}{5}C + 32 = F$. Use this equation to find the Celsius equivalent of 86°F.

_____

> **Learn About** Solving Multi-Step Problems with Decimals

Read the problem below. Then explore different ways to solve multi-step problems that involve decimals.

> Lydia is saving money for her vacation. So far she has $82.50. Each week she sets aside 25% of her paycheck for the vacation. After 8 weeks, Lydia has $338.50 saved for vacation. What is the amount of Lydia's weekly paycheck?

▶ **Model It** **You can use arithmetic to solve a multi-step problem that involves decimals.**

Total amount saved: $338.50

Amount already saved: $82.50

Amount she saved from 8 paychecks: $338.50 − $82.50 = $256

Amount she saved each week: $256 ÷ 8 = $32

Amount of weekly paycheck: 25% is $\frac{1}{4}$, so Lydia's weekly paycheck is 4 × $32, or $128.

▶ **Model It** **You can write an equation to help solve a multi-step problem that involves decimals.**

amount already saved	+	number of weeks (savings each week)	=	total amount saved
$82.50	+	8 (0.25 · x)	=	$338.50

25% of paycheck (unknown)

$82.5 + 8(0.25x) = 338.5$

$82.5 + 2x = 338.5$

Connect It   Now you will solve the equation for the problem on the previous page.

9 What can you do to get 2x alone on the left side of the equation? Fill in the blanks to show how, and then simplify.

$$82.5 - \underline{\hspace{1cm}} + 2x = 338.5 - \underline{\hspace{1cm}}$$
$$\underline{\hspace{1cm}} x = \underline{\hspace{1cm}}$$

10 What can you do to get the x alone on the left side of the equation? Fill in the blanks to show how, and then simplify.

$$2x \div \underline{\hspace{1cm}} = 256 \div \underline{\hspace{1cm}}$$
$$x = \underline{\hspace{1cm}}$$

11 Compare the arithmetic solution to solving with the equation. How are the methods similar? How are they different?

_____

_____

_____

_____

12 Describe how to solve an equation with two or more steps.

_____

_____

_____

_____

Try It   Use what you just learned to solve these problems. Show your work on a separate sheet of paper.

13 Solve. Show each step.

$0.06x - 0.18 = 0.12$

_____

_____

_____

14 Solve. Show each step.

$5.4 - 6x = -6$

_____

_____

_____

Practice **Solving Multi-Step Problems with Equations**

Study the example below. Then solve problems 15–17.

Example

Josh walked a total of 5 miles today. First he walked 1 mile from his house to the park. Then he walked laps around the $\frac{3}{4}$-mile loop trail at the park. Finally, he walked back home. How many laps did Josh walk around the trail?

You can use an equation to solve the problem.

1 mile to park + 1 mile home = 2 miles, x = number of laps

$$2 + \frac{3}{4}x = 5$$
$$2 - 2 + \frac{3}{4}x = 5 - 2$$
$$\frac{3}{4}x = 3$$
$$\frac{3}{4}x \cdot \frac{4}{3} = 3 \cdot \frac{4}{3}$$
$$x = 4$$

Solution _Josh walked 4 laps around the trail._

> The student analyzed the information in the problem and then wrote and solved an equation.

 Pair/Share
How can you check that your answer is correct?

---

15 An amusement park reduced its admission price to $15.50 per day, but now charges $1.50 per ride. Mark has $26 to spend on admission and rides. Write and solve an equation to find how many rides Mark can ride in one day.

Show your work.

> Make sure you define the variable before you write an equation.

 Pair/Share
How much more money would Mark need if he wants to ride 10 rides?

Solution _____

16 Theo made a donation to a charity. His grandfather agreed to add $4.00 to Theo's donation amount and then donate half of that sum. Theo's grandfather donated $4.25. Write and solve an equation to find the amount of Theo's donation.

Show your work.

Will you use a decimal or a fraction to represent one half?

Pair/Share
Can you solve the problem in a different way? Discuss.

Solution _____

---

17 The Hair Care Salon charges a stylist $30 per day to rent a station at the salon. Rhonda, a stylist, makes $10.50 on each haircut. Which equation will help her decide how many haircuts she must give in one day to make $138 after paying rent for her station? Circle the correct answer.

A $30h - 10.5 = 138$

B $10.5h + 30 = 138$

C $30h + 10.5 = 138$

D $10.5h - 30 = 138$

Lonnie chose **B** as the correct answer. How did he get that answer?

When a business is charged rent to operate, how does it affect the amount of money made?

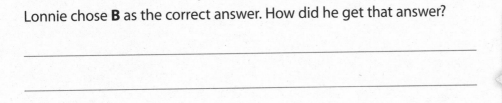

Pair/Share
Talk about how you would find the correct answer, and then identify what Lonnie might have done incorrectly.

Practice ▶ **Solving Multi-Step Problems with Equations**

Solve the problems.

1 A rectangular garden sits next to a house. Three sides of the garden are fenced, and the fourth side is the house. The length of the garden along the house is 9 meters. A total of 21.5 meters of fencing is used. If w stands for the width of the garden in meters, which equation can be used to find its width?

A $2w + 9 = 21.5$ **C** $2w - 21.5 = 9$

B $2w + 18 = 21.5$ **D** $2w + 21.5 = 18$

2 Charlie makes $34 an hour and will get a 20% raise starting next week. Choose *True* or *False* for each statement.

a. Next week, Charlie's new hourly wage will be 120% of his original wage.   ☐ True   ☐ False

b. Next week, Charlie's new hourly wage will be $40.80.   ☐ True   ☐ False

c. Next week, Charlie will be making $6.80 less than his current hourly wage.   ☐ True   ☐ False

d. Next week, Charlie will be earning an additional 20 cents per hour.   ☐ True   ☐ False

3 Sammy incorrectly solves the equation $\frac{1}{3}(x + 9) = 8$. Her work is shown below.

a. Which step shows an error based on the equation only from the previous step? Select all that apply.

A Step 1: $\frac{1}{3}x + 9 = 8$

B Step 2: $\frac{1}{3}x = 8 + 9$

C Step 3: $\frac{1}{3}x = 17$

D Step 4: $x = 17 \div 3$

E Step 5: $x = 5\frac{2}{3}$

b. What is the correct solution to the original equation? _____

4 Banners at the school store were on sale for $3 off the regular price. Louis bought 4 banners on sale and paid a total of $18. Write and solve an equation to find the regular price of one banner.

Show your work.

Answer _____

5 The length of each of the two congruent sides of an isosceles triangle is $2x + 3$. The length of the third side is $2x$. Its perimeter is 36 centimeters. Draw and label this triangle. Write an equation that could be used to find the value of x. Solve for x and then find the length of all three sides.

Show your work.

Answer _____

 **Self Check** Go back and see what you can check off on the Self Check on page 125.

Use What You Know

You've learned how to solve two-step equations. Take a look at this problem.

Mr. Thomas brings $100 to a fundraiser. He wants to leave the event with at least $50 in his pocket. Guests at the fundraiser buy raffle tickets for several different prizes. Each raffle ticket costs $2.50. How many raffle tickets can Mr. Thomas buy and still leave with at least $50 in his pocket?

Use math you already know to solve the problem.

a. How much money does Mr. Thomas have at the start of the fundraiser? _____

b. Let t = the number of tickets bought. Write an expression to show how much it costs to buy t tickets. _____

c. Use the expression above to write a different expression that shows how much money Mr. Thomas would have left after buying t tickets. _____

d. Suppose Mr. Thomas buys 25 tickets. How much money would he have left? Is this at least $50? Show your work.

_____

e. Suppose Mr. Thomas buys 20 tickets. How much money would he have left? Is this at least $50?

_____

f. What is the greatest number of tickets Mr. Thomas can buy and still have at least $50 left? Explain. _____

_____

g. Could Mr. Thomas buy fewer than 20 tickets? Explain.

_____

_____

h. Fill in the blank. Mr. Thomas could buy any number of tickets that is _____ or fewer.

You can solve the problem on the previous page by writing and solving an inequality.

starting amount	−	ticket price	·	number of tickets	is at least	amount left
100	−	2.5	·	t	≥	50

Solving a two-step inequality is similar to solving a two-step equation. But, when you multiply or divide each side of the inequality by a negative number, you reverse the inequality symbol.

$$100 - 2.5t \geq 50$$

$$100 - 100 - 2.5t \geq 50 - 100$$

$$-2.5t \geq -50$$

$$\frac{-2.5t}{-2.5} \leq \frac{-50}{-2.5} \quad \textbf{(Reverse the symbol.)}$$

$$t \leq 20$$

He can buy 20 or fewer tickets.

Let's use integer inequalities to examine why the symbol is reversed. A is −3 and B is 3, so, $A < B$. On the number line, A is to the left of 0 and B is to the right.

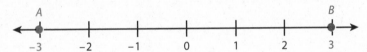

Now **divide both A and B by −1** and compare the values. A becomes 3 and B becomes −3. Now $A > B$ and A is to the right of 0 and B is to the left.

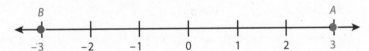

After dividing by a negative number, the quotient is on the opposite side of 0, which means the symbol is reversed.

Reflect

1 What is the effect of multiplying both sides of an inequality by a negative number? Explain, and give an example.

_____

_____

Learn About ▶ **Solving Two-Step Inequalities**

Read the problem below. Then explore different ways to solve a two-step inequality.

> Chang has at most $60 to spend on socks and sneakers. He finds a pair of sneakers that he likes for $36. If socks are $3 per pair, how many pairs of socks could Chang buy?

▶ **Model It** **You can write and solve an inequality to understand the problem.**

The price of the sneakers and socks combined must be $60 or less.

price of sneakers	+	$3 \cdot p$ pairs socks	must be < or =	$ Chang has
36	+	$3p$	$\leq$	60

$$36 + 3p \leq 60$$
$$36 - 36 + 3p \leq 60 - 36$$
$$3p \leq 24$$
$$\frac{3p}{3} \leq \frac{24}{3}$$
$$p \leq 8$$

▶ **Model It** **You can graph the solution set on a number line.**

The inequality $p \leq 8$ means all values less than or equal to 8. However, in this situation, only whole numbers make sense. You cannot buy a fraction of a pair of socks, or a negative number of pairs of socks.

Connect It
Now you will look at the solution and graph to analyze and interpret the inequality.

2 What does the inequality statement in *Model It* mean?

_____

_____

3 List the steps for solving this two-step inequality, using the terms constant and coefficient.

_____

_____

4 Explain why the numbers between each whole number are not a part of the solution set.

_____

_____

5 According to the graph, what is the complete solution set for the inequality?

_____

Why are −1 and −2 not in the solution set? _____

_____

6 How do you graph the solution set of an inequality when that set includes only

whole numbers? _____

_____

Try It
Use what you just learned about inequalities to solve these problems. Show your work on a separate sheet of paper.

7 Students in the garden club are planting a spring flower garden in the town square. They have already spent $80 of the $200 budget. Write and solve an inequality to show how many $30 packs of bulbs they can buy. _____

8 Draw a number line and graph the solution set.

Learn About ▶ **Solving Multi-Step Inequalities**

Read the problem below. Then explore different ways to solve a multi-step inequality.

Mrs. Sanchez is building a laundry room in the basement of the apartment building she owns. Given the layout of the basement, she wants the width of the room to be 20 feet and the length to be longer than the width. If she wants the area of the room to be more than 500 square feet, what could be the length? Look at the diagram Mrs. Sanchez drew.

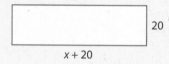

$x + 20$ 20

▶ **Model It** **You can write and solve an inequality to find x.**

The product of the width and length must be greater than 500 square feet.

width	•	length	more than	area
20	•	$(20 + x)$	>	500

$$20(20 + x) > 500$$

$$400 + 20x > 500$$

$$400 - 400 + 20x > 500 - 400$$

$$20x > 100$$

$$\frac{20x}{20} > \frac{100}{20}$$

$$x > 5$$

▶ **Model It** **You can graph the solution set for x on a number line.**

In this problem situation, the numbers in the solution can be whole numbers, decimals, or fractions. You can measure to a fraction of a foot or inch and that measurement could be used to solve the problem. So, the graph shows a solid line.

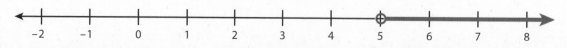

Connect It Now you will look at the solution and graph to analyze and interpret the inequality.

9 Describe in words what the inequality statement in the first *Model It* means. _____

_____

10 What do you do with any value for x in the solution set to find the length? Explain.

_____

11 Look at the graph of the solution set. Why is there an open circle on the 5? Why is there a solid line instead of just circles on the whole numbers?

_____

_____

_____

12 The numbers on the number line end at 8. The arrow shows that numbers beyond 8 are also in the solution set. Given the problem situation, do you think the solution set can extend forever, or will there be a limit? Explain. _____

_____

13 In words, describe what the solution set is and what it means in context of the problem.

_____

_____

_____

Try It Use what you just learned about inequalities to solve this problem. Show your work on a separate sheet of paper.

14 Solve $8(12 - \frac{1}{4}x) \geq 82$ and graph the solution set on a number line.

_____

Practice ▶ **Solving Multi-Step Inequalities**

Study the example below. Then solve problems 15–17.

Example

At the beginning of baseball season, Coach Thorne takes inventory of the team equipment to see what he needs. He counts 24 baseballs, but he needs to start off the season with at least 100 balls. The balls that he uses are sold in packages of 4. How many packages could the coach buy?

Look at how you could show your work by solving an inequality.

$$24 + 4x \geq 100$$
$$24 - 24 + 4x \geq 100 - 24$$
$$4x \geq 76$$
$$\frac{4x}{4} \geq \frac{76}{4}$$
$$x \geq 19$$

Solution _Coach Thorne could buy 19 or more packages._

The inequality shows that the 24 balls the coach has plus x packages of 4 balls each must be greater than or equal to 100 balls.

Pair/Share

How would the inequality change if the problem said "more than 100 balls?"

---

15 Market and More is having a cereal sale. Every box of cereal is $0.60 off the regular price. Jane has $10 and she wants to buy 4 boxes of the same cereal. She uses the inequality below to determine the regular price of cereal that she can afford. Solve the inequality and explain what the solution means.

$4(r - 0.6) \leq 10$, where r = regular price

Show your work.

Four times the sale price of the box has to be ten dollars or less.

Solution _____

_____

_____

Pair/Share

Try some different prices in the solution set and discuss the results.

16 Solve the inequality and graph the solution set on a number line.

$200 - 4.5x \le 20$

Show your work.

What happens when you multiply or divide both sides of an inequality by a negative number?

Pair/Share
Talk about situations that this inequality might represent.

Solution _____

---

17 Greg calculated that he had to drive at least 50 miles per hour on the highway to get to his destination in the time that he has. Which number line shows the solution set to this inequality?

Think about what "at least" means in the context of the problem.

A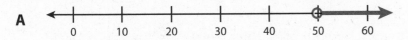

B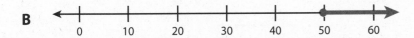

C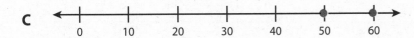

D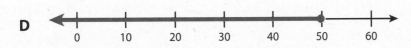

Jess chose **C** as the correct answer. How did she get that answer?

_____

_____

_____

Pair/Share
Discuss what the graph in **C** means.

Practice ▷ Solving Multi-Step Inequalities

Solve the problems.

1 You need to reverse the symbol to solve which inequality?

A $4(5 - y) \geq 80$

C $3y - 4 , > 1$

B $2(y - 3) \geq 8$

D $-\frac{3}{4} + 6y > \frac{1}{4}$

2 The number line shows the solution set to which inequality?

A $12 + 4x > 22$

B $3x + 2 \geq 17$

C $12 + 4x \geq 22$

D $4x - 12 \leq 22$

3 Sally wants to spend no more than $16 on school supplies. The table shows how much each item costs at the school store. No tax is charged.

Item	Price
Loose leaf	$2.55/package
Pen	$1.22/pen
Binder	$3.99/binder
Eraser	$0.67/eraser

Which combination of items can Sally buy? Select all that apply.

A 6 loose leaf and 6 pens

D 4 loose leaf and 8 erasers

B 8 pens and 8 erasers

E 2 loose leaf and 3 binders

C 3 pens and 4 binders

F 3 binders and 6 erasers

4 A salesperson is paid $60 per week plus $4.50 per sale. This week, the salesperson wants to earn at least $250. How many sales, *n*, must the salesperson make in order to meet that goal?

Write in each box the appropriate given number, operation, or symbol that creates an inequality to determine the minimum number of sales, *n*, the salesperson must make.

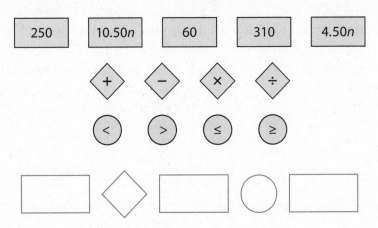

5 Raj has a $25 budget to spend on decorations for a party. He has already spent $18.60. He now wants to get some helium balloons that cost $0.80 each. Write and solve an inequality to show the number of balloons that Raj could buy.

Show your work.

Answer Raj can buy _____ balloons.

6 Graph the solution set for the inequality in problem 5. Describe what the solution means and how the number of balloons bought will affect the amount in the budget.

Show your work.

Answer _____

_____

_____

_____

✓ **Self Check**   **Go back and see what you can check off on the Self Check on page 125.**

Lesson 17 Solve Problems with Inequalities   **165**

Solve the problems.

1 Jill always buys the same kind of shampoo in an 11.5-ounce bottle. She is at the store buying more and sees that the bottle is now bigger and has 20% more for the same price. How many ounces of shampoo are in the new bottle?

A 11.5

B 13.8

C 17.3

D 23.0

2 Mark incorrectly solved the inequality $-4\left(\dfrac{5}{2} + \dfrac{3}{2}x\right) > 8$. His work is shown.

Part A Which step shows an error based on the inequality only from the previous step? Select all that apply.

A Step 1: $-10 + 6x > 8$

B Step 2: $6x > 8 - 10$

C Step 3: $6x > -2$

D Step 4: $x > -\dfrac{1}{3}$

Part B What is the correct solution to the original inequality? _____

3 Luke's baseball team went to an amusement park at the end of the season. The cost of admission for 5 coaches and 12 players was $407.50. The admission cost for each coach was $27.50. What was the admission cost for each player?

A $22.50

B $23.97

C $27.50

D $31.67

4 Which scenario represents the expression $4x - 4$? Select *Yes* or *No* for each scenario.

a. Jack earns $4 per hour but owes his parents $4; x represents the number of hours he works.

☐ Yes   ☐ No

b. Alex is 4 years older than 4 times Ava's age; x represents Ava's age.

☐ Yes   ☐ No

c. A store has a 4% discount on gloves; Mike bought x pairs of gloves at $4 a pair.

☐ Yes   ☐ No

d. Jane bought x number of tickets at $4 each and had a coupon for $4 off the total cost.

☐ Yes   ☐ No

5 Bobby is hanging a cabinet above the washer and dryer in the laundry room. The cabinet is $3\frac{1}{2}$ feet wide and 2 feet tall. If he wants to center the cabinet horizontally on a wall that is $6\frac{1}{4}$ feet wide, how far will the end of the cabinet be from the edge of the wall?

Show your work.

Answer _____

6 Lauren says the two expressions $3x + 4(2x + 5)$ and $6x + 5x + 5$ are equivalent.

Part A Simplify the expressions to determine whether or not Lauren is correct.

Show your work.

Answer _____

Part B Substitute a number for the variable to determine whether or not Lauren is correct.

Show your work.

Answer _____

Performance Task

Answer the questions and show all your work on separate paper.

Rocky's parents are buying him a cell phone. His parents told him that they could budget only $1,000 this year for his cell phone and calling plan. Rocky wants to get the brand new J-phone and found three wireless companies that carry that phone. The companies each have different plans that include unlimited talk, text, and data.

Neighbors Mobile charges $180 for the J-phone and $80 per month for the calling plan. V-Cell charges $195 for the J-phone and $70 per month for the calling plan. BG&G Mobile charges the most for the J-phone at $270, but the calling plan is only $60 per month.

Which plan can Rocky's parents afford with a budget of $1,000? Write a summary for Rocky to give to his parents to explain his choice. Make sure you show your calculations and explain what they mean.

Checklist

Did You . . .

☐ Write inequalities to represent the calling plans?

☐ Use the inequalities to solve the problem?

☐ Choose a plan and support your choice?

Reflect

Reflect on Mathematical Practices After you complete the task, choose one of the following questions to answer.

- **Model** How did you decide whether to write equations or inequalities to represent the cost of the different plans?

- **Reason Mathematically** How could Rocky convince his parents that his choice will be under the budget they've set?

Unit 4
Geometry

Real-World Connection Did you know that a triangle is the strongest polygon? A triangle can't change its sides or angles without breaking at the vertices. On the other hand, a rectangle will transform into a parallelogram under pressure. The sides of the parallelogram will be congruent to the sides of the rectangle, but the angles will not be right angles. The sides of the new parallelogram will be the same, but the angle measures are now all different. A triangle will always keep its shape. Triangles are used in bridge building and in the architecture of buildings to make them strong because triangles will hold a lot of weight without collapsing.

In This Unit You will draw triangles and find the circumference and area of circles. You will use what you know about area to find the area of figures made of multiple shapes. You will also solve problems involving volume, surface area, and plane sections of solid figures.

✓ Self Check

Before starting this unit, check off the skills you know below. As you complete each lesson, see how many more you can check off!

I can:	Before this unit	After this unit
solve problems with angles	☐	☐
draw triangles to meet given conditions	☐	☐
find the area of composed figures and circles	☐	☐
solve problems with scale drawings	☐	☐
find the surface area and volume of solid figures	☐	☐
describe plane sections of prisms and pyramids	☐	☐

Problem Solving with Angles

⟳ Use What You Know

In previous grades you learned about lines and angles. Take a look at this problem.

Three lines, $\overleftrightarrow{AD}$, $\overleftrightarrow{BE}$, and $\overleftrightarrow{CF}$ intersect at point O as shown in the diagram. $\overleftrightarrow{AD}$ is perpendicular to $\overleftrightarrow{FC}$. $\angle EOD$ measures 32°. What is the measure of $\angle AOB$?

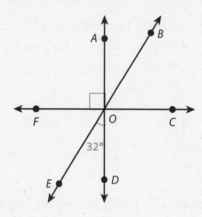

Use the math you already know to solve the problem.

a. What is the measure of $\angle FOD$? How do you know?

_____

b. Name two adjacent angles that together form $\angle FOD$. What is the sum of their measures?

_____

c. What is the measure of $\angle FOE$? Explain.

_____

d. Together, $\angle FOE$, $\angle FOA$, and $\angle AOB$ form a line or a straight angle that measures 180°. Explain how you can find the measure of $\angle AOB$.

_____

_____

On the previous page, ∠FOE and ∠EOD form a right angle. The sum of their measures is 90°. ∠FOE measures 58°, and ∠EOD measures 32°. Two angles whose measures add to 90° are **complementary angles**. Complementary angles don't have to be adjacent. ∠S and ∠T are complementary angles.

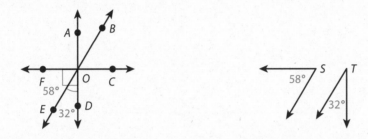

On the previous page, ∠EOA and ∠AOB form a straight line. The sum of their measures is 180°. ∠EOA measures 148°, and ∠AOB measures 32°. Two angles whose measures add to 180° are **supplementary angles**. Supplementary angles don't have to be adjacent. ∠M and ∠N are supplementary angles.

When two lines intersect, like $\overleftrightarrow{AD}$ and $\overleftrightarrow{BE}$ on the previous page, they form pairs of **vertical angles**. ∠AOB and ∠EOD are vertical (or opposite) angles. They are the non-adjacent angles formed by the intersecting lines. Vertical angles have the same measure. Both ∠AOB and ∠EOD measure 32°.

▶ **Reflect**

1 Look at the diagram on the previous page. What can you say about ∠FOE and ∠BOC? What can you say about ∠AOB and ∠BOC?

_____

_____

_____

Learn About ▶ **Using Supplementary and Vertical Angles**

Read the problem below. Then explore how to use facts about supplementary and vertical angles to find the measures of angles in a figure.

In the figure shown, what is the measure of ∠ADC?

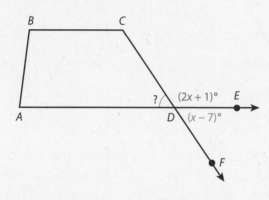

▶ **Model It** **You can use the diagram and facts about angles to write an equation.**

∠CDE and ∠EDF are supplementary angles.

(2x + 1) + (x − 7) = 180

▶ **Solve It** **You can solve the equation to find the value of x.**

2x + 1 + x − 7 = 180 _____

3x − 6 = 180 _____

3x = 186 _____

x = 62 _____

▶ **Connect It** Now you will find the measure of ∠*ADC*.

2 Look at *Model It*. How do you know that ∠*CDE* and ∠*EDF* are supplementary?

_____

3 How do you know that the measures of ∠*CDE* and ∠*EDF* add to 180°?

_____

4 Look at *Solve It*. Give reasons for the steps used to solve the equation. Write the reason next to each step.

5 Since you know that *x* = 62, what are the measures of ∠*CDE* and ∠*EDF*? Show your work.

_____

6 What is the measure of ∠*ADC*? _____ Explain your reasoning.

_____

7 What facts about angles can you use to find the unknown angle measures?

_____

▶ **Try It** Use what you just learned about supplementary and vertical angles to solve this problem. Show your work on a separate sheet of paper.

8 In triangle *ABC*, the measure of ∠*ACB* is (*x* + 11)° and the measure of ∠*ACE* is (3*x* + 5)°.

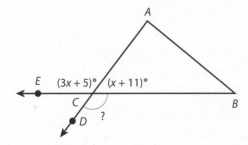

Find the measure of ∠*DCB*. _____ Find the measure of ∠*ECD*. _____

Learn About Using Complementary and Vertical Angles

Read the problem below. Then use what you know about complementary and vertical angles to find the measures of angles in the figure.

In rectangle *KLMN*, $\overline{NK}$ and $\overline{MK}$ are extended as shown in the diagram below. The measure of $\angle MKL$ is $x°$, and the measure of $\angle NKM$ is $(x + 14)°$. Find the measure of $\angle PKQ$.

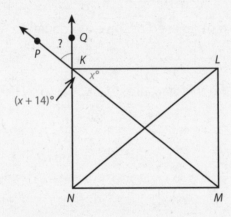

▶ **Model It** You can use the diagram and facts about angles to write an equation.

$\angle MKL$ and $\angle NKM$ are complementary angles.

$x + (x + 14) = 90$

▶ **Solve It** You can solve the equation to find the value of *x*.

$x + x + 14 = 90$	_____
$2x + 14 = 90$	_____
$2x = 76$	_____
$x = 38$	_____

Connect It Now you will find the measure of ∠PKQ.

9 Look at *Model It*. How do you know that ∠MKL and ∠NKM are complementary?

_____

10 Why do the measures of ∠MKL and ∠NKM add to 90°?

_____

11 Look at *Solve It*. Give reasons for the steps used to solve the equation. Write the reason next to each step.

12 Since you know that $x = 38$, what are the measures of ∠MKL and ∠NKM? Show your work.

_____

13 What is the measure of ∠PKQ? _____ Explain your reasoning.

_____

14 What facts about angles can you use to find the unknown angle measures on the previous page?

_____

Try It Use what you just learned about complementary and vertical angles to solve this problem. Show your work on a separate sheet of paper.

15 In rectangle *PRST*, $\overline{ST}$ and $\overline{RT}$ are extended as shown in the diagram below. The measure of ∠PTR is $x°$ and the measure of ∠RTS is $(2x - 57)°$.

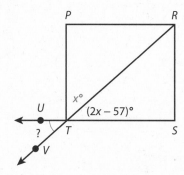

Find the measure of ∠UTV. _____ Find the measure of ∠STV. _____

Practice ▶ **Problem Solving with Angles**

Study the example below. Then solve problems 16–18.

Example

In triangle ABC, $\overline{AB}$ and $\overline{CB}$ are extended as shown. The measure of $\angle ABD$ is $(2x - 17)°$ and the measure of $\angle DBE$ is $(x + 32)°$. Find the measure of $\angle ABC$.

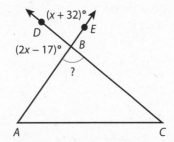

The student wrote and solved an equation using facts about supplementary and vertical angles.

Look at how you could solve this problem using the properties of supplementary and vertical angles.

$(2x - 17) + (x + 32) = 180$; $3x + 15 = 180$; $3x = 165$; $x = 55$

Solution ___$m\angle ABC = m\angle DBE = 55° + 32° = 87°$___

💬 **Pair/Share**

How can you recognize supplementary and vertical angles?

---

16 Find the value of x in the diagram below.

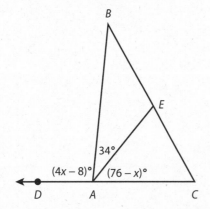

What is the measure of a straight angle?

Show your work.

💬 **Pair/Share**

How could you check your answer?

Solution _____

©Curriculum Associates, LLC   Copying is not permitted.

17 In the diagram below, $\overrightarrow{OA} \perp \overrightarrow{OC}$. Find the value of x. Show your work.

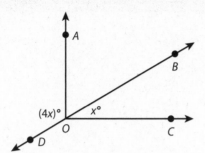

How can you express the measure of ∠ AOB?

Pair/Share
Explain the steps you took to solve the problem.

Solution _____

18 In the diagram below, $\overleftrightarrow{DE} \perp \overrightarrow{HK}$. Find the value of x. Circle the letter of the correct answer.

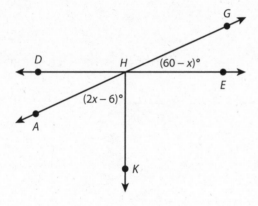

Could you use the property of vertical angles to write an equation?

A 42°

B 36°

C 33°

D 22°

Jeb chose **D** as the correct answer. How did he get that answer?

_____

_____

_____

Pair/Share
Talk about the problem and then write your answer together.

Practice ▸ **Problem Solving with Angles**

Solve the problems.

1 Find the measure of ∠AOE in the diagram below.

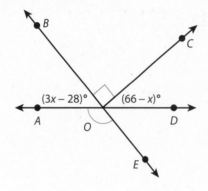

A 90°

B 100°

C 120°

D 130°

2 In the diagram below, $\overleftrightarrow{AC}$ intersects △BDE at B. Choose *True* or *False* for each statement.

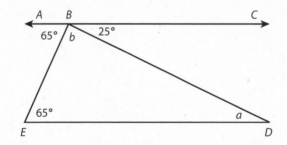

a. ∠ABE and ∠CBD are complementary.   ☐ True   ☐ False

b. 65° + b + 25° = 180°   ☐ True   ☐ False

c. ∠ABE and ∠CBD are vertical angles.   ☐ True   ☐ False

3 Four straight lines k, l, m, and n intersect as shown in the diagram. Lines k and n are perpendicular. Find x.

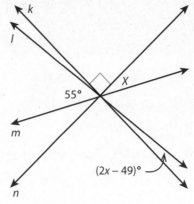

A 23°

B 28°

C 53°

D 55°

4 **Part A** Decide if each statement is always true, sometimes true, or never true. Circle your answer.

I. The sum of the measures of two supplementary angles is 90°.

      always true   sometimes true   never true

II. Two adjacent angles are supplementary.

      always true   sometimes true   never true

III. If the measure of an acute angle is represented by x, then the measure of its complement is represented by $90 - x$.

      always true   sometimes true   never true

Part B Look at your answers in Part A. If you chose "sometimes true" for an answer, draw a figure to show an example where the statement is true and another figure to show an example where the statement is not true.

✓ **Self Check** Go back and see what you can check off on the Self Check on page 169.

Lesson 18 Problem Solving with Angles **179**

Think It Through

What side lengths form a triangle?

You have worked with triangles for several years. You know they have three sides and three angles and they seem pretty simple. But, can a triangle have any side lengths? Can a triangle have any angle measures? Try an experiment. Pick random numbers, or roll a number cube and try drawing a triangle with those side lengths. You will find some combinations of side lengths form a triangle. In this lesson you will learn which combinations do or don't work as sides of a triangle.

_____

_____

_____

Can these side lengths form a triangle?

Think If you know its side lengths, you know everything about a triangle.

Cut a straw into lengths 3 cm, 4 cm, and 5 cm. Use the three pieces to form a triangle, and carefully trace the triangle on paper. Then rearrange the sides to form another triangle and trace that one too. Compare your two triangles, and compare yours to other students' triangles. Compare your triangles to the one shown here. Be sure to measure the angles with a protractor and compare the angles, too.

Trace one of your triangles next to the one shown here.

If you work carefully, you will be able to understand why we can say that if you know the side lengths you know "everything" about a triangle. Any two triangles with the same side lengths will always have the same angle measures, too.

Think If you know its angle measures, you don't know everything about a triangle.

Use a protractor to draw a triangle with one 90° angle, one 30° angle, and one 60° angle. Try to draw another triangle with the exact same angle measures, but with at least one side a different length. If you can do that, try another one.

How do these triangles compare to yours?

When you have drawn several triangles with angles measuring 30°, 60°, and 90°, compare them. Compare your triangles to the two shown here, and to other students' triangles.

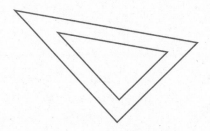

▶ **Reflect** In what way does knowing the measures of the three sides of a triangle tell you more than just knowing the measures of the three angles?

1 In what way does knowing the measures of the three sides of a triangle tell you more than just knowing the measures of the three angles?

_____

_____

_____

_____

🔍 **Let's Explore the Idea** Explore each set of conditions described below. On a separate sheet of paper draw several triangles to match the description. Then make a conjecture about the number of different triangles possible, and justify your thinking.

2 Three sides are given: Use side lengths 6 cm, 6 cm, and 4 cm. How many different triangles can you make?

_____

3 Three angles are given: Start with angle measures 80°, 40°, and 60°. Try other sets of angles such as 20°, 120°, and 40°. Try three measures that don't add up to 180°.

_____

_____

4 Two sides and the angle between them are given: Start with side lengths 5 cm and 4 cm, meeting to form a 45° angle. Then try side lengths of 2 cm and 4 cm, meeting to form a 90° angle.

_____

5 Two angles and the side between them are given: Draw triangles with a side 4 cm long and a 45° angle at each endpoint. Try different angles measures and different lengths for the side between them.

_____

_____

Now try this problem.

6 How many triangles can you draw with side lengths 2 cm, 3 cm, and 5 cm? Try sides 2 cm, 3 cm, and 8 cm. Explain what you find.

_____

_____

_____

Let's Talk About It
Solve the problems below as a group.

7 Use straws to form a quadrilateral with side lengths 5 cm, 5 cm, 3 cm, and 3 cm. Make a sketch and label the sides of your quadrilateral in the space to the right.

8 Now form different quadrilaterals using the same side lengths. Sketch and label the sides of at least two of the quadrilaterals you find.

9 Experiment with some other dimensions, such as 3 cm, 4 cm, 5 cm, and 6 cm, or 4 cm, 4 cm, 4 cm, and 4 cm. Can you find a set of 4 side lengths that will form only one quadrilateral? Explain why or why not.

_____

_____

▶ **Try It Another Way** **Work with your group to understand why triangles are used in building.**

10 When you have the three side lengths of a triangle, there is only one triangle that can be formed. How does that explain why a gate like the one here is built with a diagonal board?

_____

_____

_____

_____

Connect ▶ **Conditions for Drawing Triangles**

Talk through these problems as a class, then write your answers below.

11 Analyze Draw an isosceles triangle with exactly one 40° angle. Is this the only possibility or can you draw another triangle that will also meet these conditions? How is this different from drawing a triangle given 2 sides and the angle between them?

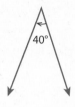

40°

_____

_____

_____

12 Explain How many different triangles can be drawn with two obtuse angles? Explain how you can be sure of your answer without drawing many examples.

_____

_____

13 Create Sketch several triangles with one side 6 cm long, one side 10 cm long, and the third side *x* cm long. What are some possible lengths of the third side? Write an inequality to express the least possible value of *x*. Write another inequality to express the greatest possible value of *x*. Use a sketch to explain your thinking.

_____

_____

_____

Apply ⟩ **Conditions for Drawing Triangles**

14 Put It Together Use what you have learned in this lesson to complete this task.

Part A Give conditions (measurements) for a triangle that would result in more than one possible triangle. Include at least one side length. Explain your thinking and provide an illustration.

_____

_____

_____

_____

Part B Give conditions for a triangle that would result in only one possible triangle. Explain your thinking and provide an illustration.

_____

_____

_____

_____

Area of Composed Figures

Use What You Know

In previous grades you learned that you can find the area of many different shapes by breaking the shapes up into rectangles and triangles. Take a look at this problem.

Maia's garden is made of rectangular regions, as shown below. She wants to cover her garden with plastic mulch to warm the soil. What is the area of her garden?

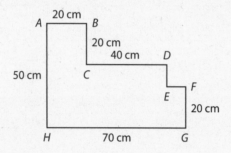

Use the math you already know to solve the problem.

a. Draw two vertical lines to break the figure up into 3 rectangles.

b. The rectangle at the left is 50 cm by 20 cm. What is its area? _____

c. One of the dimensions of the rectangle in the middle is 40 cm. What is the other dimension? Explain how you figured it out.

_____

d. What is the area of the middle rectangle? _____

e. What is the area of the rectangle at the right? Explain how you figured it out.

_____

f. How could you find the area of the figure?

_____

_____

A composite figure is a figure made up of two or more simple geometric figures such as rectangles, squares, and triangles.

To find the area of a composite figure, you can separate it into simpler shapes whose area you can find. Then add the areas together. You just need to be sure that none of the simpler shapes overlap.

There is often more than one way separate the figure into simpler shapes. Here is another way to break the figure from the previous page into three rectangles by drawing horizontal lines.

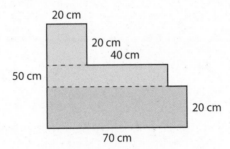

Top Rectangle

$A = lw$

$A = (20\ cm)(20\ cm)$

$A = 400$ square cm

Middle Rectangle

$A = lw$

$A = (60\ cm)(10\ cm)$

$A = 600$ square cm

Bottom Rectangle

$A = lw$

$A = (70\ cm)(20\ cm)$

$A = 1,400$ square cm

Adding together the areas of these three rectangles gives the same result.

area of the top rectangle + area of the middle rectangle + area of the bottom rectangle

400 square cm   +   600 square cm   +   1,400 square cm

The area of the composite shape is 2,400 square centimeters.

> **Reflect**

1 How does separating the composite figure into rectangles help you calculate the area?

_____

_____

_____

Learn About ▶ Dividing a Figure to Find Its Area

Read the problem below. Then explore how to calculate the area of a composite figure.

Mr. Gonzalez needs to repaint one side of his house. To decide how much paint to buy, he needs to find its area. Find the area of the figure pictured below.

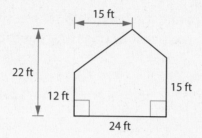

▶ **Picture It** **You can separate the figure into simpler figures and describe those figures.**

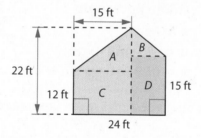

Figures **A** and **B** are right triangles.
Figures **C** and **D** are rectangles.

▶ **Solve It** **You can use formulas to find the areas of the simpler figures.**

You can find the areas of the right triangles.
Use the formula $A = \frac{1}{2}bh$.

You can find the areas of the rectangles.
Use the formula $A = lw$.

Connect It Now you will use the simpler shapes to calculate the area.

2 What are the dimensions of Triangle A? Explain.

_____

What is the area of Triangle A? Show your work. _____

3 What are the dimensions of Triangle B? Explain.

_____

What is the area of Triangle B? Show your work. _____

4 What are the areas of Rectangles C and D? Explain.

_____

_____

5 How can you find the area of the side of the house?

_____

What is that area? Show your work. _____

6 Explain how to find the area of a composite figure.

_____

_____

Try It Apply what you just learned about finding areas to the following problem. Show your work on a separate sheet of paper.

7 Describe how you could find the area of the figure below. Then find its area.

_____

_____

_____

_____

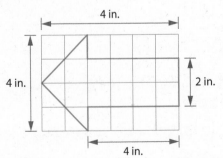

Read the problem below. Then use what you learned about calculating area to solve the problem.

The figure below shows a plan for a new town park. Park management is going to plant grass in the shaded area, at a total cost of $2.50 per square foot. How much will this project cost?

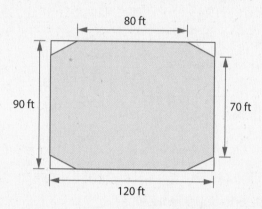

▶ **Picture It** **To find the cost, you need to know the area to be covered with grass. To find this area, you can separate the shaded figure into rectangles and triangles.**

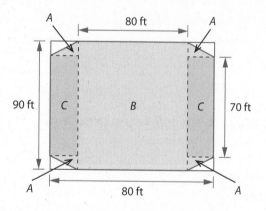

There are four right triangles that are all the same size, labeled **A**.

There is one larger rectangle, labeled **B**.

There are two smaller rectangles that are the same size, labeled **C**.

▶ **Solve It** **You can find the area of each part using the formulas for areas of triangles and rectangles.**

Area A = $\frac{1}{2}$ (10)(20) = 100 square feet

Area B = (80)(90) = 7,200 square feet

Area C = (70)(20) = 1,400 square feet

▶ **Connect It** **Now you will find the area of the shaded region and the cost of the project.**

8 Look at *Picture It*. How can you figure out the base and height of the triangles?

_____

_____

9 How can you figure out the length and width of the smaller rectangles?

_____

_____

10 Explain how to find the area of the shaded region.

_____

What is that area? Show your work. _____

11 What is the total cost of the project? Show your work. _____

You can also find area by subtracting. Think about the shaded area as the area of the outer rectangle minus the areas of the four triangles at the corners.

12 Explain how you could find the area of the shaded region by subtracting.

_____

_____

▶ **Try It** **Use what you just learned to find the area of the figure below. Show your work on a separate sheet of paper.**

13 Find the area of the hexagon at the right.
Find the area in two different ways.

_____

Practice ▶ **Finding the Area of Composed Figures**

Study the example below. Then solve problems 14–16.

Example

What is the area of this figure?

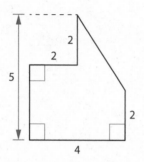

The student found the area of the figure by subtracting.

Look at how you could solve this problem by seeing the figure as a rectangle, square, and triangle.

Subtract the area of the square and the right triangle from the area of the large rectangle.

Area of the large rectangle: $(4)(5) = 20$

Area of the square: $(2)(2) = 4$

Area of the triangle: $\left(\frac{1}{2}\right)(2)(3) = 3$

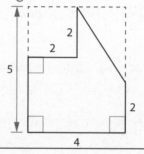

Solution $\underline{20 - 4 - 3 = 13 \text{ square units}}$

Pair/Share
What is another way to solve this problem?

---

14 The figure shows the floor plan of a carpeted area in front of a stage. How much carpeting is needed to cover this area?

Show your work.

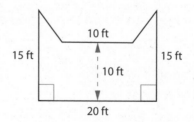

Should I add or subtract to find the area of the figure?

Pair/Share
Explain how you found the area.

Solution _____

©Curriculum Associates, LLC Copying is not permitted.

15 Jaime drew a snowflake on graph paper. What is its area in square units?

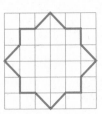

Show your work.

Solution _____

16 Which of these two kites will use more paper to make? Circle your answer.

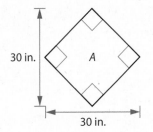   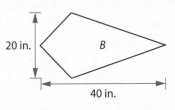

A kite A

B kite B

C They both use the same amount of paper.

D There is not enough information given.

Rudy chose **C** as the correct answer. What did he do wrong?

Practice ▶ Finding the Area of Composed Figures

Solve the problems.

1 Find the area of the pentagon in the diagram below.

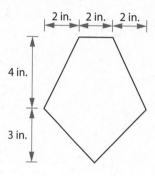

A 15 square inches

B 20 square inches

C 25 square inches

D 28 square inches

2 A contractor needs to buy grass seed to cover a lawn. The dimensions of the lawn are shown below. One bag of grass seed covers an area of 600 square yards. Shade in the minimum number of bags of seed the contractor needs to buy to cover the entire lawn.

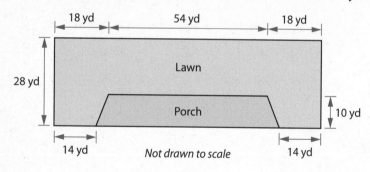

Bags of grass seed

3 The figure shown on the right is composed of two squares. The smaller square has a side length of x. The side length of the larger square measures twice that of the smaller square. Which expression accurately represents the area of the entire figure? Select all that apply.

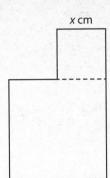

A $x + x + 2x + 2x + 2x + x + x$

B $x^2 + 2x^2$

C $(2x)(3x) - x^2$

D $x(3x) + x(2x)$

E $(x^2)(2x)^2$

4 The flag of Seychelles is shown below. The rectangular flag has a length of 3 feet and a width of 2 feet. The lines drawn from the bottom left corner to the top and right sides of the flag divide those sides into 3 equal parts. What fraction of the flag is painted red?

Answer _____ of the flag is painted red.

 Go back and see what you can check off on the Self Check on page 169.

Area and Circumference of a Circle

Use What You Know

In this lesson you will learn to find the distance around a circle and the area of a circle. Take a look at this problem.

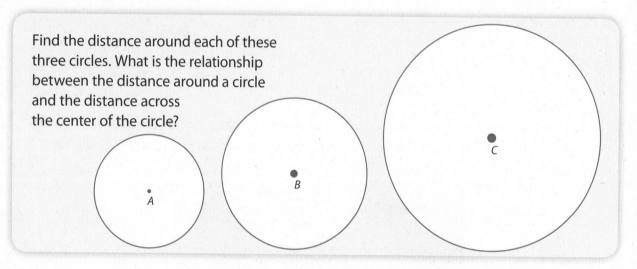

Find the distance around each of these three circles. What is the relationship between the distance around a circle and the distance across the center of the circle?

Use the math you already know to solve the problem. Record distances in centimeters.

a. Use string to measure the distance around each of the circles. Record that distance.

Circle *A* _____   Circle *B* _____   Circle *C* _____

b. Measure the distance across the circles making sure to go through the center. Record that distance.

Circle *A* _____   Circle *B* _____   Circle *C* _____

c. Divide the distance around each circle by the distance across it. Record the quotient.

Circle *A* _____   Circle *B* _____   Circle *C* _____

d. What do you notice about your answers to the last problem?

_____

e. Describe the relationship between the distance around a circle and the distance across the center of the circle.

_____

_____

For a polygon, the distance around the figure is called the perimeter. For a circle, the distance around the figure is called the **circumference**, C, of the circle.

A circle is the set of all possible points in a plane that are the same distance from a point called the **center**.

The **diameter**, d, is the distance across the circle through the center.

The **radius**, r, is the distance from the center to any point on the circle.

The diameter is twice as long as the radius. So, $d = 2r$.

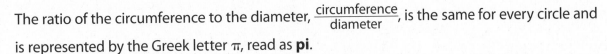

The ratio of the circumference to the diameter, $\frac{circumference}{diameter}$, is the same for every circle and is represented by the Greek letter π, read as **pi**.

$$\frac{C}{d} = \pi$$

If you multiply both sides of the equation by d, you get a formula for finding the circumference of a circle.

$$C = \pi d$$

Since the diameter is twice the radius, you can also write the formula as $C = 2\pi r$. In real-life situations, approximations for π are more useful. The decimal 3.14 and the fraction $\frac{22}{7}$ are approximations used for the number π.

▶ Reflect

1 Use your own words to explain how to find the circumference of a circle with a radius of 4 inches. Include a drawing in your explanation.

_____

_____

_____

_____

Learn About **Finding Circumference Using a Formula**

Read the problem below. Then explore how to solve the problem using the formula for the circumference of a circle.

Nadia drew a design for a copper wire sculpture as shown below. She plans to make a wire frame that includes the perimeter of the square and the circumference of the circle. She has 5 feet of copper wire. Does she have enough wire for the sculpture? Use 3.14 for π.

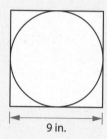

9 in.

▶ **Picture It** **You can use the diagram to determine the diameter of the circle.**

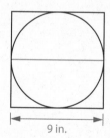

9 in.

▶ **Model It** **You can find the perimeter of the square and the circumference of the circle to figure out how much wire Nadia will need.**

Perimeter of a square = 4s where s is the length of a side of the square

$$= 4\,(9\text{ in.})$$

Circumference of a circle = πd where d is the diameter of the circle

$$= 3.14\,(9\text{ in.})$$

Connect It Now you will solve the problem from the previous page by finding the perimeter of the square and the circumference of the circle.

2 Look at *Picture It*. What is the diameter of the circle? Explain.

_____

3 How can you figure out how much wire Nadia will need for the whole frame?

_____

_____

4 How much wire will Nadia need? Show your work. _____

5 Will she have enough wire for her sculpture? Explain your reasoning.

_____

_____

6 Use your own words to explain how to find the circumference of a circle if you know the radius or diameter of the circle.

_____

_____

Try It Apply what you just learned about calculating the circumference to the following problems. Show your work on a separate sheet of paper.

7 The diameter of a basketball rim is 18 inches. Find the circumference of the rim. Use 3.14 for p. _____

8 A circular dining room table has a radius of 3 feet. If each person sitting at the table needs about 2 feet of space, how many people will fit at the table? _____

Learn About ❯ **Finding the Area of a Circle**

Read the problem below. Then explore how to find the area of a circle.

A clock face has a diameter of 10 inches. What is the area of the face of the clock? Use 3.14 for π.

▶ **Picture It** **Visualize dividing the circle into eight equal parts.**

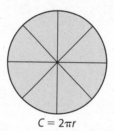

$C = 2\pi r$

▶ **Model It** **Imagine cutting out the eight parts and putting them together to make a figure that looks like a parallelogram.**

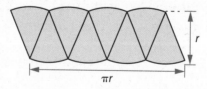

The base and height of the parallelogram relate to the parts of the circle.

The height of the parallelogram is the radius of the circle.

The base of the parallelogram is $\frac{1}{2}$ the circumference of the circle.

The formula for the area of a parallelogram is $A = bh$.

Connect It Now you will use the models from the previous page to find the area of the clock face.

9 If the diameter of the clock face is 10 inches, what is the radius? Explain your answer.

_____

10 Use the model of the parallelogram to figure out a formula for the area of a circle.

A = base of the parallelogram • height of the parallelogram

$\quad = \dfrac{1}{2}$ • the circumference of the circle • radius of the circle

$\quad = \dfrac{1}{2} \cdot 2\pi r \cdot$ _____

$\quad =$ _____

11 Use the formula to find the area of the clock face in terms of a number times π.

_____

12 Use 3.14 for π to approximate the area. Show your work.

_____

13 Explain how to calculate the area of a circle if you know the length of its diameter or its radius.

_____

_____

▶ **Try It** Apply what you just learned about calculating the area of a circle to the following problem. Show your work on a separate sheet of paper.

14 A wrestling mat used for high school competitions is shown. The wrestling circle has a diameter of 28 feet. The inner circle has a diameter of 10 feet. Use 3.14 for π. Find the area of the following:

large wrestling circle _____

inner circle _____

Learn About **Using Areas of Circles**

Read the problem below. Then use what you learned about calculating areas of circles to solve the problem.

Four circles are drawn in a square with side length 5 inches as shown below. Find the area of the shaded part of the figure.

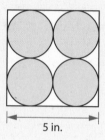

5 in.

▶ **Picture It** You can draw segment *AB* through the center of two of the circles.

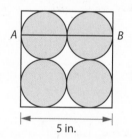

5 in.

▶ **Model It** You can use a formula to find the area of a circle.

The shaded figure consists of four circles. Remember, the area of a circle $= \pi r^2$.

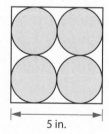

5 in.

Connect It Now you will find the area of the shaded part of the figure.

15 What can you say about the sizes of the four circles? _____

16 Look at *Picture It*. What is the relationship between the side of the square and the diameter of one of the circles?

_____

17 What is the length of the radius of each circle? Explain.

_____

_____

18 Use the formula to find the area of one of the circles. Use 3.14 for π. Round your answer to the nearest hundredth.

_____

19 What is the area of the shaded figure? _____

20 Explain how you could find the area of a figure that is formed by several same-size circles.

_____

_____

Try It Use what you just learned about calculating areas of circles to solve the problem below. Show your work on a separate sheet of paper.

21 Find the area of the shaded figure in the diagram below. Use 3.14 for π.

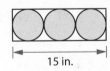

15 in.

_____

Practice Using Area and Circumference of a Circle

Study the example below. Then solve problems 22–24.

Example

A middle school is building an oval practice track with dimensions shown below. What is the distance around the track? Use 3.14 for π.

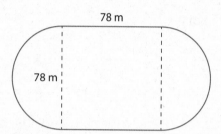

78 m

78 m

Look at how you could solve the problem by thinking about the track as a square and two semicircles.

The ends of the track are two semicircles that form a circle with diameter 78 m.

circumference = (3.14)(78) = 244.92 m

length of 2 sides of the square = 2(78) = 156 m

distance around the track = 244.92 + 156 = 400.92 m

Solution _400.92 m_

The student solved the problem by finding the circumference of a circle and adding that to the length of two sides of the square.

 Pair/Share
How could you estimate the distance to be sure that your answer makes sense?

---

22 What is the area of shaded region? Use 3.14 for π and round your answer to the nearest tenth.

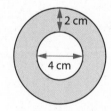

2 cm

4 cm

How can you find the radius of the larger circle?

 Pair/Share
How did you decide how to solve this problem?

Solution _____

23 The circumference of a circle is 8 inches. Find the area of the circle in terms of π.

Show your work.

If you know the circumference of a circle, how can you find the radius?

Pair/Share
If you are given the circumference of a circle, can you always find its radius? If you know the area of a circle, can you always find the circumference?

Solution _____

---

24 The stained glass window below is a semicircle. What is the distance around the window? Use π = 3.14. Circle the letter of the correct answer.

A 40.82 inches

B 66.82 inches

C 81.64 inches

D 107.64 inches

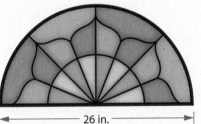

 26 in.

How many lengths do you need to consider to solve this problem?

Ari chose **D** as the correct answer. How did he get that answer?

_____

_____

_____

_____

Pair/Share
Does Ari's answer make sense?

Practice > **Using Area and Circumference of a Circle**

Solve the problems.

1 The cost of painting the circular traffic sign shown below is $3.50 per square foot. How much, to the nearest dollar, will it cost to paint the sign if its diameter measures 36 inches?

DO NOT

ENTER

A $20

B $25

C $30

D $35

2 Mack wants to calculate the circumference of a circle with a radius of 7 centimeters. Write the letter representing each calculation under the category that correctly describes whether or not the calculation on its own results in the circumference of that circle.

Finds circumference	Does not find circumference

A $2 \times 7 \times \pi$ **C** $72 \times \pi$ **E** Solve for C: $\pi = \dfrac{C}{14}$

B $2 \times 14 \times \pi$ **D** $14 \times \pi$ **F** Solve for C: $49 = C^2 \times \pi$

3 Pizza prices are based on their diameters. Below is the price list for different-sized pizza.

Whole Pizza	Price	Number of Slices
Large 18-inch	$14.75	10
Small 16-inch	$12.75	8
Personal 10-inch	$5.75	4

Based on the price list, choose *True* or *False* for each statement.

a. The unit price of the personal pizza is $0.23 per square inch. ☐ True ☐ False

b. If the 16-inch pizza is sold by the slice at $2.00 per slice, the restaurant will make a 25.5% profit. ☐ True ☐ False

c. A tray with a circumference of 32 inches is big enough to hold the personal-sized pizza. ☐ True ☐ False

d. The area of the large pizza is 2 square inches more than the area of the small pizza. ☐ True ☐ False

4 The radius of the wheel of a bicycle is 14 inches. What is the distance, in feet, that the bicycle covers after ten full rotations of the wheels? Use $\pi = 3.14$.

Answer _____

✓ **Self Check** **Go back and see what you can check off on the Self Check on page 169.**

ⓖ Use What You Know

In earlier lessons, you learned about proportional relationships. Take a look at this problem.

Suppose you want to enlarge a 4-inch by 6-inch photograph as much as possible so that it fits on a bulletin board that is 24 inches high. What is the widest the photograph can be?

6 in.

4 in.

24 in.

Not drawn to scale

Use the math you already know to solve the problem.

a. What is the ratio of the height of the original photograph to the height of the enlargement? _____

b. What is that ratio in simplest form? _____

c. You can find equivalent ratios. Complete the following table.

Height of original (in inches)	1	2	3	4	5	6
Height of enlargement (in inches)	4					

d. The relationship between the measurements of the original photograph and the enlargement is proportional. What should the width of the enlargement be? _____

e. How many times greater is the width of the enlargement than the width of the original photograph? _____

f. Explain how you could find the measurements of an enlargement if you know the ratio of the measurements of the original to the measurements of the enlargement.

_____

An enlargement is an example of a scale drawing. A **scale drawing** shows an object with its measurements in proportion to the actual measurements of the object.

A **scale** is a ratio that compares the measurements used in a scale drawing with the actual measurements. The scale used to enlarge the photograph was 1 inch : 4 inches. Scales can be given in the same units or in different units.

A **scale factor** is a constant of proportionality. When the units in the scale are the same, it tells you how many times larger or smaller the measurements of the actual object are compared to the measurements in the scale drawing. For a scale of 1 inch : 4 inches, or 1: 4, the scale factor is 4.

Scale drawings are typically used when objects are either too small or too large to be drawn at their actual sizes. Maps are scale drawings. Architects use scale drawings when they design buildings. Floor plans and maps are drawn smaller than actual size. Drawings of cells in biology are drawn larger than actual size.

The floor plan shown is an example of a scale drawing.

The scale 1 in. : 10 ft can also be written as 1 in. = 10 ft.

That means that 1 inch in the floor plan represents an actual distance of 10 feet.

1 in. : 10 ft

▶ Reflect

1 What is the scale of a drawing that shows a length of 2 inches when the actual length is 36 inches?

_____

_____

_____

Learn About > **Using Proportional Reasoning with Scale Drawings**

Read the problem below. Then explore how to use a scale drawing to find actual measurements using proportional reasoning.

Below is a scale drawing of a soccer field. A length of 1 centimeter in the drawing corresponds to 15 yards in the actual field. Find the dimensions and the area of the actual field.

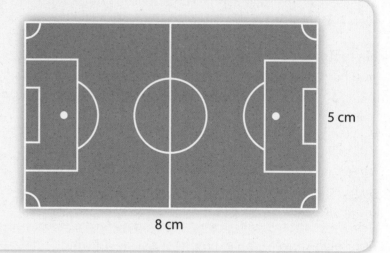

5 cm

8 cm

▶ **Measure It** **You can look at the labels to find the measurements of the drawing.**

The width of the field in the drawing is **5 cm**.

The length of the field in the drawing is **8 cm**.

▶ **Model It** **You can use the scale to make a table of equivalent ratios.**

The scale is **1 cm : 15 yd**.

Distance on the scale drawing (cm)	1	2	3	4	5	6	7	8
Distance on the actual field (yd)	15	30	45					

▶ **Model It** **You can use the scale to write equations for the ratios in a proportional relationship.**

drawing distance in centimeters → $\dfrac{1}{15} = \dfrac{5}{x}$ ← drawing distance in centimeters
actual distance in yards → ← actual distance in yards

drawing distance in centimeters → $\dfrac{1}{15} = \dfrac{8}{x}$ ← drawing distance in centimeters
actual distance in yards → ← actual distance in yards

Connect It Now you will use the models from the previous page to solve the problem.

2 Look at the first *Model It*. Complete the table. Explain how you figured out the missing lengths. _____

_____

3 Use your table to find the actual length and width of the field.

_____

_____

4 Look at the second *Model It*. Use the equations to find the actual length and width of the field.

$$\frac{1 \times 5}{15 \times 5} = \frac{5}{x} \rightarrow \frac{1}{15} = \frac{5}{\underline{\hspace{1cm}}}$$

A width of 5 centimeters on the drawing equals _____ yards on the actual field.

$$\frac{1 \times 8}{15 \times 8} = \frac{8}{x} \rightarrow \frac{1}{15} = \frac{8}{\underline{\hspace{1cm}}}$$

A length of 8 centimeters on the drawing equals _____ yards on the actual field.

5 Calculate the area of the actual field. _____

6 Explain how you can find an actual distance when you know a distance on a scale drawing and you know a scale. _____

_____

Try It Apply what you just learned about using a scale to find actual lengths to solve the following problems. Show your work on a separate sheet of paper.

7 On a scale drawing, a building is $5\frac{1}{2}$ inches tall. If the scale of the drawing is 1 in. : 8 ft, how tall is the building? _____

8 For a school project, Leo is making a model of the Statue of Liberty. He is using a scale of 2 cm : 3 m. The Statue of Liberty is 93 meters tall. How tall is Leo's model? _____

Learn About ▷ **Redrawing a Scale Drawing**

Read the problem below. Then use what you know about scale drawings to redraw a scale drawing using a different scale.

An architect is designing a recreational center for a community park. Below is her sketch of a swimming pool drawn on centimeter grid paper. The scale of the swimming pool is 1 cm : 5 m.

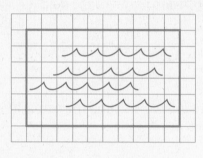

> In the architect's sketch, each small square has sides 1 centimeter in length.

Redraw the swimming pool using a scale of 1 cm : 10 m.

▶ **Picture It** **You can compare the measurements in the original scale drawing to the measurements in the new scale drawing.**

In the new scale, 1 centimeter represents a longer distance than it did in the old scale.

original |—— 1 cm ——|—— 1 cm ——|
5 m   5 m
10 m

new scale |—— 1 cm ——|
10 m

The measurement of each side in the new scale drawing is half as long as the measurement of the original scale drawing.

Connect It Now you will solve the problem on the previous page and show that the actual dimensions of the pool are the same for both scale drawings.

9 Each square on this grid represents 1 centimeter. Draw the swimming pool on the previous page using the scale 1 cm : 10 m.

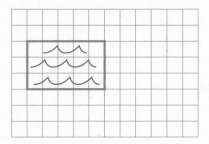

10 Calculate the actual dimensions of the swimming pool using the original scale, 1 cm : 5 m.

_____

_____

11 Calculate the actual dimensions of the swimming pool using the new scale, 1 cm : 10 m.

_____

_____

12 Explain how you can tell if your new scale drawing is correct.

_____

Try It Use what you just learned about redrawing a scale drawing using a different scale. Show your work on a separate sheet of grid paper.

13 The scale of the rectangle at the right is 0.5 cm : 4 ft. The length of each square on the grid represents 0.5 cm.

a. Draw the same rectangle using the scale 0.5 cm : 2 ft.

b. Find the area of the actual rectangle. _____

Practice ▶ **Using Scale Drawings**

Study the example below. Then solve problems 14–16.

Example

The Laerdal Tunnel in Norway is the world's longest tunnel. It is 24.4 km long. An engineer plans to make a scale model of the tunnel using the scale 3 cm : 4 km. What will the length of the model be?

Look at how you can solve the problem by writing an equation to show the proportional relationship.

drawing (cm) ⟶ $\frac{3}{4} = \frac{x}{24.4}$ ⟵ drawing (cm)
actual (km) ⟶ ⟵ actual (km)

$\frac{3 \times 6.1}{4 \times 6.1} = \frac{x}{24.4}$

$3(6.1) = 18.3$

Solution _The length of the model will be 18.3 cm._

The student wrote a proportion and found a ratio equivalent to $\frac{3}{4}$ with a denominator of 24.4.

 Pair/Share
How could you tell if your answer is reasonable?

---

14 The aquarium has a scale model of a great white shark for sale in their gift shop. If the scale of the model is 2 in. : 7 ft, what is the actual length of the shark?

What does 5 inches represent?

├─────────── 5 in. ───────────┤

 Pair/Share
Explain the steps you used to solve this problem.

Solution _____

©Curriculum Associates, LLC   Copying is not permitted.

15 The scale used to make a scale model of a car is 1 : 18. The length of the model is $9\frac{1}{2}$ inches. How many feet long is the actual car?

9 $\frac{1}{2}$ in.

The length of the model is given in inches but the question asks for an answer in feet.

Pair/Share

If the scale were 1 : 24, would the model car be larger or smaller than this one?

Solution _____

---

16 A floor plan of a house was drawn using a scale of 1 cm = 1.5 m. The family room in the plan is pictured as 5 cm by 4 cm. In square meters, what is the actual area of the family room? Circle the letter of the correct answer.

A 20

B 27

C 30

D 45

Liz chose **C** as the correct answer. How did she get that answer?

_____

_____

_____

Would drawing a diagram help?

Pair/Share

If you know the length and width of a scale model or drawing, what other information do you need to find the actual length and width?

Practice **Using Scale Drawings**

Solve the problems.

1 The Gomes family is on a road trip. On the first day, they drove a distance shown as $3\frac{1}{2}$ inches on a map. The actual distance that they drove was 245 miles. Which is the scale of the map?

A 1 in. : $3\frac{1}{2}$ mi

B 1 in. : 7 mi

C 1 in. : 70 mi

D $3\frac{1}{2}$ in. : 70 mi

2 The shaded part of the diagram below shows the area of a bathroom. The length of one grid square corresponds to 1.5 feet in the actual bathroom. The floor will be covered with ceramic tiles that are 6 inches by 6 inches. How many tiles are needed to cover the bathroom floor?

A 48

B 56

C 84

D 252

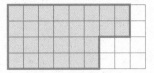

3 John has a map that shows a rectangular park with a circular pond. The scale on the map is $1\frac{1}{4}$ cm : 8 yd. On the map, the width of the park is $2\frac{1}{2}$ cm, and the length is $6\frac{1}{4}$ cm. The pond has a diameter of $1\frac{1}{4}$ cm. Use 3.14 for p.

Complete the following sentences and round to the nearest square yard.

The area of the actual park is _____ square yards.

The area of the actual pond is _____ square yards.

4 A contractor is building a fence around a square garden that has a side length of 3 inches in a scale drawing. The scale factor of the drawing is $1\frac{1}{2}$ inches : 4 feet. If one link of fence measures $2\frac{2}{3}$ feet, shade the correct number of links needed to build a fence around the entire garden.

3 in.

Scale $1\frac{1}{2}$ in. = 4 ft

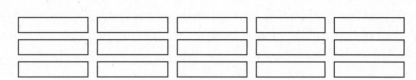

Each link of fence = $2\frac{2}{3}$ ft

5 Justin made a scale drawing of a sailboat he saw at the harbor. The length of the actual boat is 24 feet, and the mast is 20 feet high. In Justin's sketch, the boat is 2 centimeters longer than the mast. What is the length of the boat on his sketch?

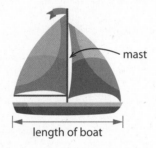

mast

length of boat

Answer _____

✓ **Self Check** **Go back and see what you can check off on the Self Check on page 169.**

Lesson 23 · Introduction
Volume of Solids

⟳ Use What You Know

In grade 6, you learned to find the volumes of rectangular prisms and of solid figures composed of rectangular prisms. Take a look at this problem.

Find the volume of the figure shown.

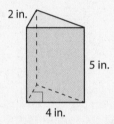

2 in.

5 in.

4 in.

Use the math you already know to solve the problem.

a. This figure is a right triangular prism. Imagine two prisms attached together like this:

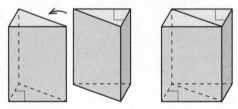

b. Describe the composed figure.

_____

c. What are the dimensions of the composed figure?

_____

d. What is the volume of the composed figure?

_____

e. How could you find the volume of the triangular prism you started with? Explain.

_____

_____

A **right prism** is a solid that has two faces (called bases) that are polygons. The bases of a right prism are the same size and shape and parallel to each other. The other faces are rectangles and are perpendicular to the bases. Prisms are named by their bases. Here are some examples of right prisms.

Triangular Prism

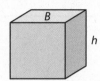

Rectangular Prism

Pentagonal Prism

To find the volume of the triangular prism on the previous page, you multiplied the three dimensions of the rectangular prism and took half, or divided the product by 2.

So, the formula for the volume of a triangular prism is $\frac{1}{2}\ell wh$ or $\left(\frac{1}{2}\ell w\right)(h)$. The expression $\frac{1}{2}\ell w$ represents the area of the triangle, the base of the prism.

To find the volume of a right triangular prism, find the area of the triangular base, the number of cubes in one layer, and multiply by the height, the number of layers.

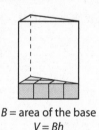

$B =$ area of the base
$V = Bh$

▶ Reflect

1 Do you think you can use the formula $V = Bh$ to find the volume of any right prism? Explain.

_____

_____

_____

Lesson 23 Volume of Solids   **219**

Learn About ▷ Finding Volume of Prisms

Read the problem below. Then explore how to calculate volume using the formula for the volume of right prism.

A packing carton in the shape of a triangular prism is shown in the diagram below. What is the volume of this carton?

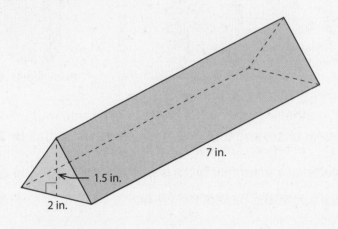

7 in.

1.5 in.

2 in.

▶ **Model It** **You can use words to describe the prism.**

The base of this prism is a triangle.

The base of the triangle measures 2 inches.

The height drawn to the base of the triangle measures 1.5 inches.

The height of the prism is 7 inches.

▶ **Solve It** **You can use the formula $V = Bh$ to find the volume of the carton.**

You know the height of the prism.

You need to find the area of the base shown below.

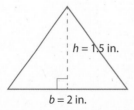

$h = 1.5$ in.

$b = 2$ in.

Connect It Now you will solve the problem from the previous page.

2 Look at *Model It*. How do you know which faces of the carton are the bases?

_____

3 Describe the shapes of the other faces.

_____

4 Which of the dimensions of the other faces do you use to find the volume of the prism? Explain.

_____

5 What is the area of the base of the carton? Show your work.

_____

6 What is the volume of the carton? Show your work.

_____

7 How can you find the volume of any triangular prism?

_____

_____

Try It Apply what you just learned about finding volume to the following problem. Show your work on a separate sheet of paper.

8 What is the volume of the right triangular prism shown below? _____

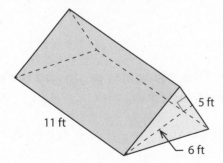

11 ft   5 ft   6 ft

Learn About > # Finding Volume of Complex Solids

Read the problem below. Then use what you learned about calculating volumes of prisms to solve the problem.

What is the volume of the camping tent shown below?

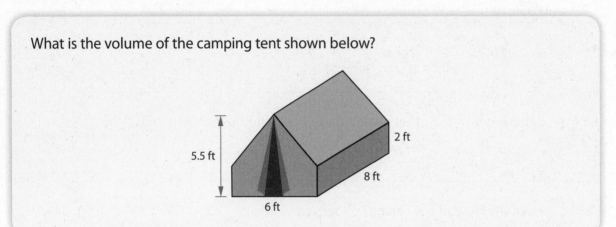

5.5 ft
2 ft
8 ft
6 ft

▶ **Model It** **You can think about this figure as the combination of two solids: a triangular prism on top of a rectangular prism.**

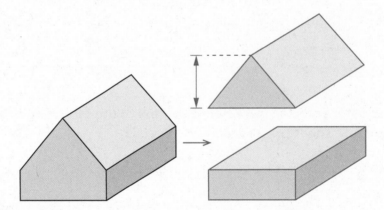

▶ **Solve It** **You can find the volume of the triangular prism and the volume of the rectangular prism and add the volumes together.**

volume of the triangular prism = area of the triangular base × height of the prism

volume of the rectangular prism = area of the rectangular base × height of the prism

Connect It Now you will solve the problem from the previous page.

9 Look at *Model It*. What are the dimensions of the rectangular prism? _____ × _____ × _____
Label the figure to show the dimensions. What is its volume? Show your work.

_____

10 What are the dimensions of the base of the triangular prism? Label the figure to show the dimensions.

_____

Explain how you found the height of the triangular base.

_____

_____

11 What is the volume of the triangular prism? Show your work.

_____

12 What is the volume of the tent? _____

13 Sam says that he can find the volume of the tent without breaking it up into two different solids. Explain how.

_____

_____

14 How do you find the volume of a figure made up of two or more prisms?

_____

Try It Use what you just learned about calculating volume to solve the problem below. Show your work on a separate sheet of paper.

15 Mr. Jones is building the garage shown to the right. What is the volume of the garage? _____

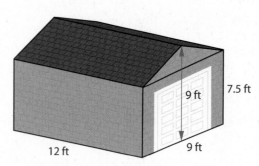

7.5 ft

9 ft

12 ft

9 ft

Practice ▶ **Finding Volume of Solids**

Study the example below. Then solve problems 16–18.

Example

How much gas (in cubic inches) would fill this gas can?

Look at a side view to see how you could find the area of the base of the prism by breaking it into two rectangles and a right triangle.

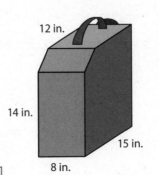

The student found the volume by multiplying the area of the base times the height.

The area of triangle A is $\frac{1}{2}(3)(3) = 4.5$ square inches.

The area of rectangle B is $3(12) = 36$ square inches.

The area of rectangle C is $14(15) = 210$ square inches.

The area of the base is $4.5 + 36 + 210 = 250.5$ square inches.

Solution $V = Bh = (250.5)(8) = 2,004$ cubic inches

💬 **Pair/Share**
How could you break up this figure into three different prisms to find the volume?

---

16 A bicycle ramp used for competitions is a triangular prism. What is the volume of the ramp?

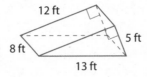

Which lengths are the base and height of the triangular base?

💬 **Pair/Share**
How do you decide which faces are the bases of the prism?

Solution _____

17 Find the volume of the Canada Post mailbox shown below.

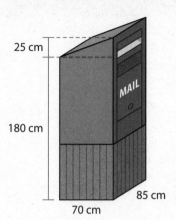

25 cm

180 cm

70 cm

85 cm

MAIL

What shapes make up this solid?

Pair/Share
Explain the steps you took to solve the problem.

Solution _____

---

18 A machine part is made from a rectangular prism with a smaller rectangular prism cut out of it, as shown below. What is the volume of the part? Circle the correct answer.

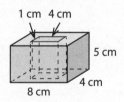

1 cm   4 cm

5 cm

4 cm

8 cm

Should I add or subtract to find the volume of the machine part?

A   20 cubic centimeters

B   140 cubic centimeters

C   160 cubic centimeters

D   180 cubic centimeters

Leo chose **D** as the correct answer. How did he get that answer?

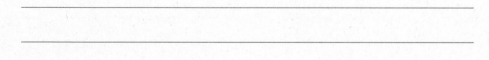

Pair/Share
Does Leo's answer make sense?

Practice ▸ Finding Volume of Solids

Solve the problems.

1 What is the volume of the bird house shown below?

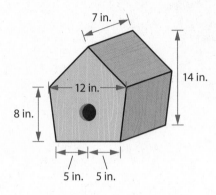

A 1,120 cubic inches

B 980 cubic inches

C 892 cubic inches

D 868 cubic inches

2 Janet needs to purchase one of the shipping containers below. Write the words "Large," "Medium," and "Small" under the appropriate container based on their volumes.

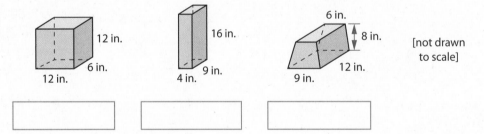

[not drawn to scale]

3 Two water tanks are shown. Tank A is a rectangular prism and Tank B is a triangular prism. Tank A is filled with water to the 6-meter mark. Some of the water from Tank A is being transferred to Tank B so that the water level in Tank A is at 2 meters. Shade the amount of water in Tank B to indicate the approximate height of the water in Tank B after the transfer. Also write the height, to the nearest whole number of meters, in the answer box provided.

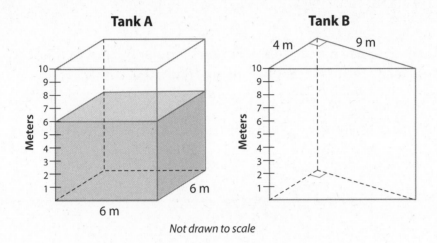

Tank A

Tank B

6 m

6 m

4 m

9 m

Not drawn to scale

In Tank B, the height of the water is approximately _____ meters.

4 The base of a right triangular prism is a right isosceles triangle whose equal sides measure 25 cm each. The volume of the prism is 0.075 cubic meter. Find the height of the prism.

Answer _____

✓ **Self Check** **Go back and see what you can check off on the Self Check on page 169.**

🔄 Use What You Know

In grade 6, you learned to use nets to represent rectangular prisms. In this lesson, you will learn to find surface area of rectangular prisms and other right prisms.

Find the surface area of the building block in Ben's construction set shown below.

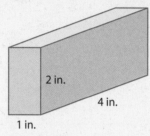

2 in.

4 in.

1 in.

Use the math you already know to solve the problem.

a. How many faces does the block have? What shape are the faces?

_____

b. Draw the top and bottom faces and label their dimensions.

c. Draw the front and back faces of the block and label their dimensions.

d. Draw the side faces and label their dimensions.

e. How could you find the surface area of the block?

_____

The surface area of a three-dimensional figure is the sum of the areas of all its faces. A rectangular prism has three pairs of faces that are the same size and shape.

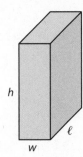

The **top and bottom** faces have the same area: $A = \ell w$.

The **front and back** faces have the same area: $A = hw$.

The **left and right** side faces have the same area: $A = h\ell$.

To find the surface area of a rectangular prism, add the areas of all six faces.

Surface Area = ℓw + ℓw + hw + hw + $h\ell$ + $h\ell$

             top   bottom   front   back   left side   right side

         = $2\ell w + 2hw + 2h\ell$

▶ **Reflect**

1 How can you find the surface of area of a cube with edge length 3 in.?

_____

_____

_____

Learn About ▶ **Surface Area of a Triangular Prism**

Read the problem below. Then explore different ways to calculate the surface area of a triangular prism.

How many square feet of nylon fabric would be needed to make the camping tent shown below including the floor?

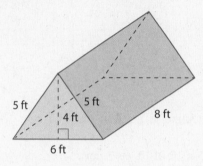

5 ft   5 ft   8 ft   4 ft   6 ft

▶ **Picture It** **You can draw and label the dimensions of the five faces of this prism.**

The tent is in the shape of a right triangular prism. The bases of the prism are two triangles that are the same size and shape.

The other faces of the prism are three rectangles:

5 ft   8 ft   5 ft   8 ft   6 ft   8 ft

▶ **Solve It** **You can use formulas to find the areas of the faces.**

Area of a rectangle with length, ℓ, and width, w:

$A = \ell w$

Area of a triangle with base, b, and height, h:

$A = \frac{1}{2} bh$

Connect It Now you will use the model and formulas to find the surface area and solve the problem.

2 How can you find the areas of the faces of the prism? _____

_____

3 Do you have to find the areas of five different figures? Explain your thinking.

_____

_____

4 What is the area of a triangular base? Show your work.

_____

5 What are the areas of the rectangular faces? Show your work.

_____

6 How could you find the surface area of the tent? _____

_____

_____

7 Use your own words to explain how to find the surface area of a right triangular prism.

_____

_____

Try It Use what you just learned about finding the surface area of a triangular prism to solve the following problems. Show your work on a separate sheet of paper.

8 Find the surface area of the prism. _____

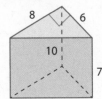

9 Suppose a cube has the same surface area as the prism in problem 8. Find the edge length of the cube.

_____

Learn About ▷ **Surface Area of a Complex Solid**

Read the problem below. Then use what you learned about calculating surface areas of prisms to solve the problem.

Mrs. Anderson wants to buy a glass greenhouse with the dimensions shown. The greenhouse will not have a floor. What is its surface area?

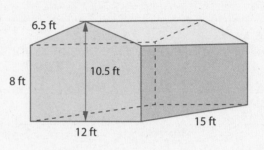

▶ **Picture It** **You can draw and label the dimensions of the faces of this prism.**

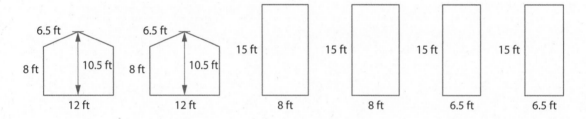

▶ **Model It** **You can find the area of one of the bases by breaking it into a rectangle and a triangle.**

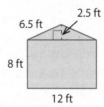

▶ **Solve It** **You can use formulas to find the area of each of the faces.**

Area of a rectangle with length, ℓ, and width, w:

$A = \ell w$

Area of a triangle with base, b, and height, h:

$A = \frac{1}{2} bh$

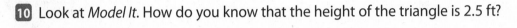

Connect It Now you will use the models and formulas to find the surface area of the greenhouse.

10 Look at *Model It*. How do you know that the height of the triangle is 2.5 ft?

_____

_____

11 What is the area of one of the bases of the prism? Show your work and explain your reasoning.

_____

_____

12 Describe the other faces of the prism, including their dimensions. _____

_____

13 What is the surface area of the greenhouse? Show your work.

_____

14 Explain how to find the surface area of any right prism. _____

_____

Try It Use what you just learned about calculating surface area to solve the problem below. Show your work on a separate sheet of paper.

15 Find the surface area the prism shown below. Include all faces, even the bottom.

_____

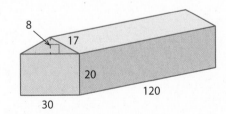

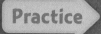
Practice ▶ **Finding Surface Area of Solids**

Study the example below. Then solve problems 16–18.

Example

Jing put two identical building blocks on top of each other. The dimensions of each block were 2 in. by 2 in. by 4 in. What is the surface area of the resulting prism?

Look at how you could show your work by drawing a model.

There are 4 faces that are
2 in. by 8 in. and 2 faces that are
2 in. by 2 in.

Surface Area = 4(2)(8) + 2(2)(2)
             = 64 + 8

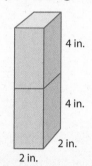

4 in.

4 in.

2 in.

2 in.

Solution ___72 square inches___

The student found the dimensions of the new figure and found its surface area.

💬 **Pair/Share**
Why can't you find the surface area of each block and double it?

---

16 Find the surface area of the prism shown below.

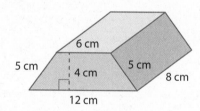

6 cm

5 cm   4 cm   5 cm

12 cm   8 cm

Show your work.

How many faces does this prism have?

💬 **Pair/Share**
What information do you need to find the surface area of any prism?

Solution _____

17 How much wrapping paper would you need to cover a rectangular box that is 19 inches by 12 inches by 3 inches if you need 10% more wrapping paper than the surface area of the box? Give your answer to the nearest square inch.

Show your work.

Would drawing a model help?

Pair/Share
How could you check to see if your answer is reasonable?

Solution _____

---

18 Find the surface area of the solid below. Circle the letter of the correct answer.

A 32.5 in.²

B 210 in.²

C 225 in.²

D 240 in.²

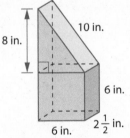

8 in.

10 in.

6 in.

6 in. $2\frac{1}{2}$ in.

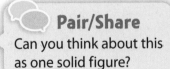

What two solids make up this three-dimensional figure?

Alex choose **D** as the correct answer. What did she do wrong?

_____

_____

_____

_____

Pair/Share
Can you think about this as one solid figure?

Practice ▶ **Finding Surface Area of Solids**

Solve the problems.

1 Two cubes with edge lengths of 3 centimeters and 2 centimeters are placed on top of each other as shown. What is the surface area of the resulting figure?

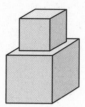

A 65 cm²　　　　**C** 74 cm²

B 70 cm²　　　　**D** 78 cm²

2 An artist is commissioned to build two hollow glass sculptures standing vertically, one in the form of a triangular prism and one in the form of a rectangular prism. Their dimensions are shown below.

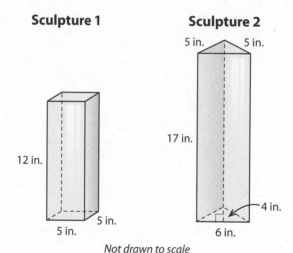

Not drawn to scale

Choose *True* or *False* for each statement.

a. The volume of Sculpture 1 is greater than the volume of Sculpture 2.

☐ True　　☐ False

b. The surface area of Sculpture 2 is less than the surface area of Sculpture 1.

☐ True　　☐ False

c. The base of Sculpture 1 covers a larger area than the base of Sculpture 2.

☐ True　　☐ False

d. Sculpture 1 requires more glass to complete than Sculpture 2.

☐ True　　☐ False

3 The prism below has dimensions 2 inches by 3 inches by 4 inches. To the right of the prism, shade the number of prisms necessary, if stacked on top of each other as shown, to create a new prism with a surface area between 100 square inches and 130 square inches.

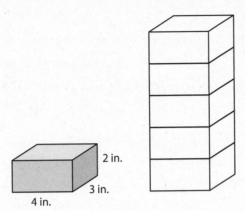

4 Mario's father is building a skateboard ramp in the shape of a triangular prism. Mario has agreed to paint the ramp once it's finished. If a quart of paint covers 85 square feet, how many whole quarts of paint will Mario need to buy? (Mario doesn't have to paint the bottom of the ramp.)

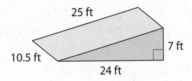

Show your work.

Answer Mario needs to buy _____ whole quarts of paint.

✓ Self Check   Go back and see what you can check off on the Self Check on page 169.

Understand Plane Sections of Prisms and Pyramids

💭 Think It Through

What is a cross-section of a three-dimensional figure?

You can think about a cross-section as a slice through a three-dimensional figure. Picture slicing a cube made up of clay with a string. The two-dimensional shape that you get is called a **cross-section**. When you slice through a cube, one of the shapes that you could get is a triangle.

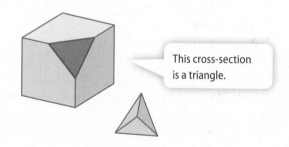

This cross-section is a triangle.

A three-dimensional figure can have many different cross-sections. It all depends on the direction or angle of the slice.

Think Different slices through a rectangular prism create different shapes

One way to slice a rectangular prism is with a plane parallel to a base of the prism.

✏️ **Circle** the words or phrases that describe the types of slices you can make.

Another way to slice a rectangular prism is with a plane perpendicular to a base of the prism.

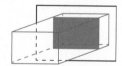

The slice could also look like this. It doesn't have to be parallel or perpendicular to a face of the prism.

One way to slice a rectangular pyramid is with a plane parallel to the base of the pyramid.

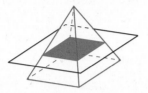

The slice can be parallel to the base, perpendicular to the base, or at a completely different angle.

Another way to slice a rectangular pyramid is with a plane perpendicular to the base. If the plane goes through the top vertex, the slice could look like this.

If the plane is perpendicular to the base but doesn't go through the top vertex, the slice could look like this.

The slice doesn't have to be parallel or perpendicular to a face of the pyramid. It could look like this.

▶ Reflect

1 How can you use the formula for the volume of a cylinder to remember the formulas for the volume of a cone and the volume of a sphere?

_____

_____

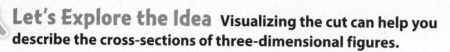

Let's Explore the Idea **Visualizing the cut can help you describe the cross-sections of three-dimensional figures.**

The figures shown are right rectangular prisms.

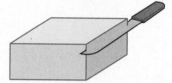

2 Think about slicing a cake or a block of cheese. If your slice is horizontal, or parallel to the base of the prism, what shape do you think the cross-section will be?

_____

3 If your slice is vertical, or perpendicular to the base of the prism, what shape do you think the cross-section will be?

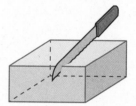

_____

4 Look at a cross-section of a rectangular prism shown below. Describe how you could cut the prism to get a triangle for the cross-section.

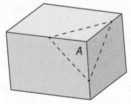 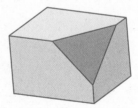

A

_____

Now try these problems.

5 Suppose you cut this rectangular pyramid by slicing it parallel to its base. What shape do you think the cross-section will be?

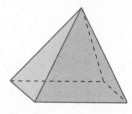

_____

6 How could you slice the pyramid and get a triangle for the cross-section?

_____

Let's Talk About It
Solve the problems below as a group.

7 Look at problem 2. When a slice is made parallel to the base of a rectangular prism, do you think you will always get a rectangle? If your answer is yes, describe the rectangle. If your answer is no, describe the other types of polygons you can get.

_____

8 Look at problem 4. Do you think you can get different types and sizes of triangles when you slice a rectangular prism? Explain your thinking.

_____

_____

9 Look at this cross section of a cube. Describe how you can slice a cube and get a hexagon for a cross-section.

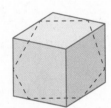 

_____

_____

Try It Another Way Work with your group to explore cross-sections of cylinders and cones.

10 Describe the shapes you would get if you slice a cylinder with a plane parallel to the base or with a plane perpendicular to the base.

_____

_____

_____

11 What can you say about the shapes you could get if you slice a cone with a plane parallel to the base?

_____

_____

_____

Connect > **Plane Sections of Prisms and Pyramids**

Talk through these problems as a class, then write your answers below.

12 Compare   Picture slicing a rectangular pyramid and a cone with a plane parallel to the base. How are the cross-sections the same? How are they different?

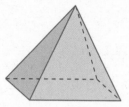 

_____

_____

_____

13 Analyze   The base of the pyramid shown is a square with an area of 64 square inches.

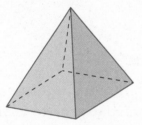

a. Suppose that the pyramid is sliced so that the cross-section is a square with an area of 49 square inches. What can you say about how to slice the pyramid to get that square?

_____

_____

_____

b. Suppose the pyramid is sliced so that the cross-section is a trapezoid. What can you say about how to slice the pyramid to get a trapezoid?

_____

_____

Plane Sections of Prisms and Pyramids 243

14 Put It Together Use what you have learned to complete this task.

> The figure shown below is a cube.
>
>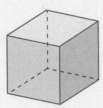

Part A Which of the following cross-sections can you get when you slice a cube? Write *possible* or *not possible* next to each figure named.

square _____

circle _____

rectangle that is not a square _____

pentagon _____

Part B Choose two of the shapes that you decided are possible to get. Circle your choices. Then describe how you would slice the cube to get that cross-section. You can use a drawing to help explain, if needed.

Solve the problems.

1 Hanley made a scale drawing of his rectangular patio for a landscaping project. In the drawing, he used a scale of 1 inch = 5 feet. The dimensions of the patio in the scale drawing are 5.5 inches by 4 inches. What is the actual area of the patio?

A 22 square feet

B 95 square feet

C 110 square feet

D 550 square feet

2 If you slice a rectangular pyramid parallel to its base, what will be the shape of the cross-section?

A square

B triangle

C trapezoid

D rectangle

3 The measures of two vertical angles are represented by $(4x - 7)°$ and $(2x + 13)°$. What is the sum of the two angle measures?

A 33°

B 45°

C 66°

D 90°

4 What is the volume of the following triangular prism?

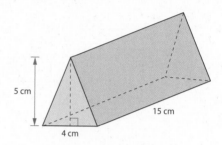

The volume of the prism is _____ cm³.

5 A jeweler created a pendant using 24 centimeters of silver wire for a square and enough gold wire to form the largest circle possible that fits inside the square. To design the circle, the jeweler used 3.14 to estimate π. Choose *True* or *False* for each statement.

a. The measure of the circle's diameter is equal to the measure of one of the square's sides.

☐ True ☐ False

b. The length of wire needed for the square exceeds the length needed for the circle by about 5.16 centimeters.

☐ True ☐ False

c. The area of the square exceeds the area of the circle by about 7.74 square centimeters.

☐ True ☐ False

d. If the dimensions of the square are doubled, the area of the circle will double.

☐ True ☐ False

6 The angles below share a common vertex.

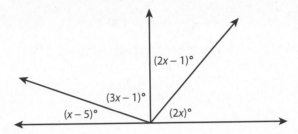

$(2x - 1)°$

$(3x - 1)°$

$(x - 5)°$

$(2x)°$

What are the measures of all four angles?

Show your work.

Answer _____

7 ✏️ It is possible to make a triangle that is both an isosceles triangle and a right triangle.

Part A Draw an isosceles right triangle.

Part B Is it possible to draw an isosceles right triangle with side lengths of 15, 20, and 25? Explain.

_____

_____

_____

_____

Performance Task

Answer the questions and show all your work on separate paper.

Austin is making a frame for a storage container to use in his backyard for tools and sports equipment. He would like it to be a rectangular prism with two square faces. Austin has 60 feet of metal tubing to make the frame. He wants the container to have the greatest possible volume. Find two possible sets of dimensions for Austin's frame.

Share your dimensions with the rest of your class and see if your class can find the dimensions that will make the container with the greatest possible volume. If you were Austin, would you choose to make the storage container with these dimensions or different dimensions? Explain.

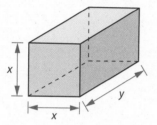

Reflect

Reflect on Mathematical Practices After you complete the task, choose one of the following questions to answer.

- **Model** What expressions can help you solve the problem?

- **Use Structure** Does a smaller square base and longer sides make a larger volume? Or, does a larger square base and shorter sides make a larger volume? What patterns do you see?

Unit 5
Statistics and Probability

Real-World Connection The school cafeteria director wants to know which meal is most popular: pizza, fish sticks, or macaroni and cheese. Will she need to ask the opinion of all 520 students in your school to make a decision?

Asher wonders if 7th graders are taller in his 2013 class than the 7th graders that were in the class of 2001. After he gathers all of the data, how will he answer his question?

In This Unit You will learn about random samples and how to make inferences from statistical information. You will also study probability as well as different ways to compare data.

✔ Self Check

Before starting this unit, check off the skills you know below. As you complete each lesson, see how many more you can check off!

I can:	Before this unit	After this unit
identify random samples	☐	☐
make statistical inferences from random samples	☐	☐
compare data with measures of center and variability	☐	☐
find probabilities of single and compound events	☐	☐
compare theoretical and experimental probabilities	☐	☐

Think It Through

> **How can you use samples to get information about a population?**

A food service company supplies meals for 12 different schools. How might the company get information about students' favorite lunches? Surveying every student in every school would take a lot of time and effort. It would be more efficient to survey a **random sample** that represents the whole group, or **population**. What makes a sample representative of the population?

Each rectangle below contains squares, circles, and triangles. The rectangle on the left shows the shapes scattered randomly. The rectangle on the right shows the shapes somewhat grouped. The circled group in each rectangle represents a sample.

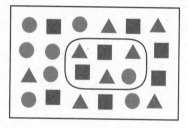   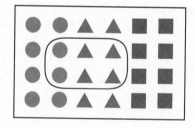

A sample that selects items from an evenly distributed group is representative of the population.

A sample that looks at the group from a sorted, uneven mix may not be representative of the population.

Think How do you find a random sample for a population?

In order for a sample to be considered random, every object or event has to have an equal chance of being selected. Look at the picture of the jar, which contains names of all students at Center School.

✏️ **Underline** the sentence that explains why selecting ten names from the top of the jar might be considered a biased sample.

Suppose you pick ten slips of paper from the top of the jar. Do all names have an equal chance of being selected? Maybe the slips at the top belong to the last class that put their names in the jar. Selecting from the top does not give the names at the bottom of the jar an equal chance. This would be a **biased sample** because it does not represent the whole population.

Suppose, instead, that you put your hand in and mix the slips all around. You do this each time you pick the ten names. With this method, all names get an equal chance of being selected. This would be a random sample.

Here are some ways to select a representative random sample.

- Use a pattern, such as selecting every fourth person who enters the cafeteria.

- Use a method, such as drawing names out of a hat, where everyone has an equal chance of being selected.

- Divide the population into groups, such as by grade level, and randomly select people from each group.

Here are some ways of selecting a sample that might result in a biased sample.

- Let people volunteer to take a survey.

- Choose people who are easy to reach, such as the students who happen to be in the cafeteria when you are available to give surveys.

- Choose people as a group, such as students on the honor roll.

Think **How can you use data collected from a random sample?**

You can use data from a random sample to generalize about a population. Maybe about half of the students in the sample say that pizza is their favorite school lunch. You might predict that about half the population has the same preference. The data collected from the sample might be used for making menu choices and for determining food orders.

▶ **Reflect**

1 What do you think would be a good way to select a random sample of all the students at the 12 schools in the school district mentioned on the previous page?

_____

_____

🔍 **Let's Explore the Idea** **Read the problem and answer the questions.**

Carla has a list of all 720 students in her middle school. She writes the name of each student on a slip of paper and puts each slip in a box. Then she pulls 30 names from the box to decide who she will survey about the upcoming school election.

2 How many students are in Carla's sample? _____

How many students are in the population? _____

3 What are different attributes of students or different groups of students that should be represented in the sample?

_____

_____

_____

A graphing calculator or spreadsheet can be used to create a list of random numbers.

12	164	47	598	306	702
92	7	99	388	141	85
584	163	414	373	627	417
121	71	549	480	154	90
35	419	88	660	279	349

4 Describe one way you could use this list of numbers to choose the students for a sample.

_____

_____

5 Does using random numbers generated by a calculator to decide who to survey give everyone in the population an equal chance of being selected? Why or why not?

_____

_____

_____

Let's Talk About It
Solve the problems below as a group.

6 One of Carla's friends suggests that she survey only eighth-graders because they are the oldest and probably know more about the election than younger students. Do you think this suggestion creates a random sample? Explain.

_____

_____

7 Another one of Carla's friends suggests that she make the sample larger and survey 100 students. Which sample size is more likely to represent the population? Explain.

_____

_____

_____

_____

Try It Another Way Work with your group to decide if the methods for selecting a sample are fair or biased. Give reasons for your answers.

8 The events committee wants to survey students about a school dance. The committee is meeting in the gym, where the girls' basketball team is practicing. They survey the players on the girls' basketball team.

_____

_____

_____

9 A store owner wants to survey customers about the products he sells. He programs the computer to select 100 customers from the mailing list and sends them each a survey.

_____

_____

Connect > Identifying Random and Biased Samples

Talk through these problems as a class, then write your answers below.

10 Compare The teachers in a school are asked to send four students from their homerooms to represent the class.

Method 1	**Method 2**	**Method 3**
Ms. Rose puts the names of all the girls in a box and chooses two without looking. Then she does the same for the boys' names.	Mr. Burr sends the four students sitting closest to the door.	Mrs. Rosati puts the names of all the students in a box, mixes the names, and pulls out four names without looking.

Compare the selection methods. Do you think each one creates a random or biased sample? Which is more likely to be representative? Explain.

_____

_____

_____

_____

11 Explain The producers of a television singing contest are conducting a survey on their website to see who viewers think should win the competition. Julie says that this method will create a random sample of the people who watch the show. Do you agree?

_____

_____

_____

12 Plan Describe a way to find a random sample of 100 homeowners from your community to complete a survey about recycling.

_____

_____

_____

13 Put It Together Use what you have learned to complete the task.

> The manager at Fitness Forever wants to add some new types of fitness classes and possibly remove others. He wants to offer a variety of classes that will appeal to all gym members.

Part A What would you consider to be a representative sample of this population?

_____

_____

_____

Part B Describe how you would create a random sample of the gym population to participate in a survey about fitness classes.

_____

_____

_____

_____

_____

Part C Describe at least two different samples for this population that could be considered biased and explain why they might be biased.

_____

_____

_____

_____

🔄 Use What You Know

In Lesson 26 you learned about random samples. In this lesson you will look at random samples to make predictions. Take a look at this problem.

> Ms. Jennings held a "mystery bag" full of marbles up in front of her class. She said, "There are 100 marbles in this bag. Some are red, and all of the others are blue. I want you to estimate how many red marbles are in the bag without looking in the bag and counting all of them." She then let Joe pick 10 marbles from the bag without looking.

Use the math you already know to solve the problem.

a. Suppose Joe had 4 red marbles in his sample. Write a ratio representing the number of red marbles in Joe's sample.

_____

b. If Joe is not allowed to pull out any more marbles, what do you think his best estimate will be for the total number of red marbles in the mystery bag? Explain. _____

_____

c. Ms. Jennings had Joe put his 10 marbles back in the bag and shook it up. Then she let Angela pull 10 marbles from the bag without looking. Angela had 6 red marbles in her sample. Why do you think Angela's sample was different from Joe's? _____

_____

d. If Angela is not allowed to draw any more samples, and she does not know about Joe's sample, what do you think her best estimate would be for the total number of red marbles in the mystery bag? Explain. _____

_____

e. Ms. Jennings had Angela put her marbles back in the bag, shook the bag up again, and let Isabella reach in and draw out 10 marbles without looking. Isabella got 9 reds in her sample. Why might Isabella's sample be different from Joe's and Angela's?

_____

_____

Random samples can differ from one another due to **random variation**. The amount of variation may be small, as in the difference between Joe's and Angela's samples from the mystery bag. Occasionally, the variation is much larger, as in the difference between Joe's and Isabella's samples.

In order to get a better estimate of the number of red marbles in the mystery bag, one thing that can help is to draw more random samples. That would help you judge how typical the samples from Joe, Angela, and Isabella are. If you see a number of samples clustering around the same value, you can be more confident about using that value to estimate what you would like to know about the population.

Random sampling is helpful in situations beyond the mystery bag scenario. It can be useful, for example, when conducting surveys. Suppose, for example, you want to make a prediction about who will win a school election, but you don't have the time or resources to survey everyone in school. You could draw a random sample of names from a list of students in school and administer the survey to them. The random sample could be as large as time and resources allow.

▶ Reflect

1 Suppose Joe, Angela, and Isabella had drawn samples of 25 marbles instead of 10. How might this change their results?

_____

_____

_____

| Learn About | **Representing Distributions of Statistics** |

Read the problem below. Then explore different ways to represent distributions of statistics from random samples.

> Ms. Jennings decided to let all 20 students in her class draw random samples from the mystery bag. Each student was allowed to draw a sample of 10 marbles, count the number of reds in the sample, and then put the 10 marbles back in the bag. Angela thinks the extra samples will help the class make a better estimate of the number of reds in the mystery bag. How should students organize their results to get a good estimate?

▶ **Model It** **Joe suggested organizing the results in the following table.**

	1	2	3	4	5	6	7	8	9	10	11	12	13	14	15	16	17	18	19	20
Number of Reds	8	10	7	10	7	5	9	8	7	9	7	6	8	8	4	7	5	9	8	6
Proportion of Reds	0.8	1.0	0.7	1.0	0.7	0.5	0.9	0.8	0.7	0.9	0.7	0.6	0.8	0.8	0.4	0.7	0.5	0.9	0.8	0.6

The table shows the proportion of reds obtained in each sample.

▶ **Model It** **Angela thought it would be easiest to organize the data with a dot plot.**

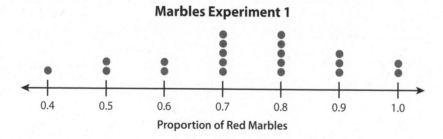

Marbles Experiment 1

Proportion of Red Marbles

▶ **Model It** **Isabella decided to construct a box plot to organize the class data.**

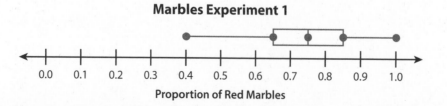

Marbles Experiment 1

Proportion of Red Marbles

Connect It   Now you will represent your results of taking random samples.

2 Make your own mystery bag with 100 marbles (or similar objects). Decide how many objects will be red and how many will be blue. Record the number of reds in the bag and the number of blues in the bag here. _____

3 Pretend to be each of the 20 students in Ms. Jennings' class. Repeat the experiment. Take 10 marbles out of the bag without looking. Count the number of reds and record that number in a table. Replace the marbles and repeat until you have 20 samples.

4 Use your table to make a dot plot.

_____

5 Use your dot plot to make a box plot.

_____

6 Imagine someone who doesn't know how many red marbles you put into the mystery bag. Which representation (table, dot plot, or box plot) would best help them estimate the number of reds in the mystery bag? Explain.

_____

_____

Try It   Use what you just learned about representing data to solve this problem.

7 Suppose one of your classmates used a different number of reds. Her dot plot is shown below. What is a good estimate for the number of reds in her bag? Explain.

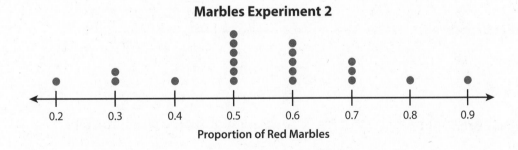

Marbles Experiment 2

Proportion of Red Marbles

_____

_____

_____

Learn About ▶ **Comparing Samples of Different Sizes**

Read the problem below. Then explore different ways to compare distributions of statistics from random samples when the samples are different sizes.

> Angela asked Ms. Jennings if they could re-do the mystery bag activity. Angela wanted to change just one thing about it: she asked if each student could draw 20 marbles instead of just 10 marbles. Ms. Jennings agreed, and the class re-did the activity in the way Angela asked. How do the results of this new activity compare to the results of the previous one?

▶ **Model It** **You can stack dot plots to compare the two distributions of results.**

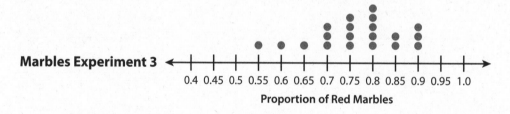

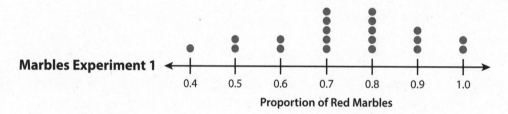

▶ **Model It** **You can stack box plots to compare the two distributions of results.**

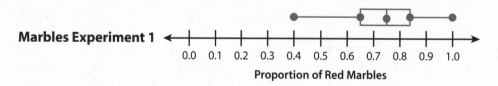

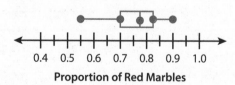

Connect It Now you will use the dot plots and box plots to compare the two data distributions.

8 Look at the models on the previous page. Compare the shapes of the two distributions of data shown in the dot plots from the two experiments.

_____

9 Compare the centers of the two distributions to one another.

_____

_____

_____

10 Compare the spreads. Which distribution is more spread out? Why?

_____

_____

11 If you could only take one sample from the mystery bag in order to make a prediction, would you rather draw a sample of 10 marbles or a sample of 20 marbles? Explain your choice by referring to the representations of the two distributions.

_____

_____

_____

Try It Use what you just learned about data distributions to solve this problem.

12 Perform the activity again, but this time draw 20 samples of only 5 marbles each. Record your results in a dot plot. How does the distribution compare to the dot plots you produced when you drew samples of 10?

_____

_____

_____

Practice **Making Statistical Inferences**

Read the example below. Then solve problems 13–15.

Example

Tammy was running for class president. She wanted to know if she had a good chance of winning the election, so she decided to have her friends help her with surveys.

Jonathan surveyed a random sample of 10 students from the school. 7 of them said they would vote for Tammy. If there are 230 students in the school, and all of them vote, what is Jonathan's best estimate of the number of students who would vote for Tammy?

Look at how you could show your work.

$\frac{7}{10}$ of the students said they would vote for Tammy.

$\frac{7}{10} = 0.7$

$0.7 \times 230 = 161$

Solution ___161___

Jonathan used the ratio of students who said they would vote for Tammy in his sample to make a prediction about the whole population.

 Pair/Share
Why is it important to have random samples rather than just samples you pick out on your own students to survey?

---

13 Kimberly had more time to conduct surveys and decided to survey a random sample of 30 students from the school. In Kimberly's sample, 24 students said they would vote for Tammy. What is Kimberly's best estimate of the number of students in the school who would vote for Tammy?

Sampling lets us make predictions about an entire population without surveying everyone.

 Pair/Share
What are some reasons someone would have to draw a small sample rather than a large one?

Solution _____

14 Who is likely to have a better estimate of the number of students who will vote for Tammy: Jonathan or Kimberly? Explain your choice by using what you learned in this lesson.

Whose sample size was larger?

Solution _____

_____

_____

_____

Pair/Share
How big do you think a "good" random sample has to be?

15 Which size random sample is likely to provide the most trustworthy results?

A 5

B 10

C 30

D There is no difference.

How does sample size affect results?

Katie chose **D** as the correct answer. How did she get that answer?

_____

_____

_____

_____

_____

_____

Pair/Share
How would you help Katie understand her error?

Practice ▸ **Making Statistical Inferences**

Solve the problems.

1 Jamie wanted to estimate the mean word length in her science textbook. She did not have time to count every word and compute the average, so she took a random sample of 50 words. Which of these is the best thing to do to estimate the mean word length in the book?

A Find the average word length for the words in her sample and then multiply by 50.

B Find the average word length for the words in her sample and use it as the prediction for average word length for the entire book.

C Use a smaller sample of words to reduce the amount of spread in the distribution of averages.

D Draw a random sample of 50 words from a different science textbook and compare the new results to the original results.

2 A representative sample of 60 students from a high school is surveyed. Each student is asked which elective he or she is taking. The table shows the responses.

Elective	Number of Students
Dance	19
Music	7
Art	15
Photography	11
Electronics	8

Based on the survey results, choose *True* or *False* for each statement.

a. There are many excellent dancers at the school. ☐ True ☐ False

b. About 25% of the students at the high school are taking art. ☐ True ☐ False

c. In a group of 30 students, it is expected that 11 of the students are taking photography. ☐ True ☐ False

d. Next year, 7 out of every 60 students will be taking music. ☐ True ☐ False

e. In a group of 120 students, it is expected that 16 of the students are taking electronics. ☐ True ☐ False

3 Kayla developed a study to determine the populations of fish in a lake. She took two random samples in the winter and again in the summer. She organized her data in the following table.

	Trout	Whitefish	Walleye	Total Sample
Winter	42	44	14	100
	46	42	12	100
Summer	91	84	25	200
	85	89	26	200

What valid inference can Kayla make about the entire fish population in the pond? Select all that apply.

A The total number of fish in the pond is 600.

B The walleye population comprises anywhere from 12% to 14% of the total population in both the winter and summer.

C The number of white fish in the pond is greater than the number of trout.

D The ratios of the populations of trout, whitefish, and walleye are relatively stable regardless of which season the samples were taken.

4 Suppose you flipped a fair coin 15 times. Then, 11 of your friends did the same thing. Without actually flipping a coin, make a table to show a realistic set of data for this situation. Your table should show the percentage of heads obtained by each person doing the coin flips.

Organize the data in the table you constructed using a dot plot.

Suppose you and each of your friends decided to flip the coin 50 times each instead of 15. Explain how the dot plot above would change and sketch a predicted dot plot for the situation below.

_____

_____

✓ **Self Check** **Go back and see what you can check off on the Self Check on page 247.**

Using Mean and Mean Absolute Deviation to Compare Data

Use What You Know

In this lesson, you will compare two distributions by looking at their centers and variabilities. Take a look at this problem.

Marcus is the basketball reporter at Chesapeake State University. He wants to write a story comparing the heights of players on the men's team to the heights of players on the women's team. He made two dot plots to help him compare heights.

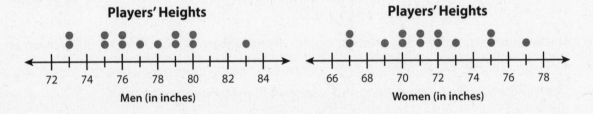

Use the math you already know to solve this problem.

a. What are some heights that you see only on the men's team? What are some heights you see only on the women's team?

_____

b. What are some heights that you see on both the men's team and the women's team?

_____

c. Estimate the typical height for the men's team. Mark it on the graph. Do the same for the

women's team. _____

d. How does the typical height for the men's team compare to the typical height for the

women's team? _____

_____

e. How does the spread for the distribution of heights on the men's team compare to that of

the women's team? _____

_____

_____

For data sets like the ones on the previous page, it can be helpful to compute the measures of center and compare them against your estimates.

One measure of center you can use for each data set is the **mean**. For the men's basketball team, the mean height is 77.2 inches (rounded to the nearest tenth). For the women's basketball team, the mean height is 71.5 inches (rounded to the nearest tenth).

You can also compare estimates of spread against a formal measure. One measure of spread is the **mean absolute deviation (MAD)**. The MAD describes the average distance between the data values in a distribution and the mean of the distribution. To compute the MAD for the men's team, start by subtracting each data value from the mean.

Height	78	76	73	76	80	77	75	83	79	79	75	73	80
Difference from Mean	−0.8	1.2	4.2	1.2	−2.8	0.2	2.2	−5.8	−1.8	−1.8	2.2	4.2	−2.8

Then, you can average the absolute values of all of those results to get the MAD:

$$\frac{0.8 + 1.2 + 4.2 + 1.2 + 2.8 + 0.2 + 2.2 + 5.8 + 1.8 + 1.8 + 2.2 + 4.2 + 2.8}{13} = 2.4$$

You can use the same procedure to compute the women's team's MAD, which in this case would equal 2.3 (rounded to the nearest tenth).

The difference between the mean heights of the teams is about 6 (77.2 − 71.5).

The MAD for the two distributions are about the same (between 2.3 and 2.4).

6 is a little more than two times 2.4, so the difference between the means is a little more than twice the value of the MAD for each distribution. If the difference between the means was three or more times as great as the MAD for each distribution, there would be an even greater difference between the mean heights. A dot plot would show fewer heights in common between the men's and women's teams.

▶ **Reflect**

1 How would the distributions change if the difference between the means was the same as the MAD for each distribution?

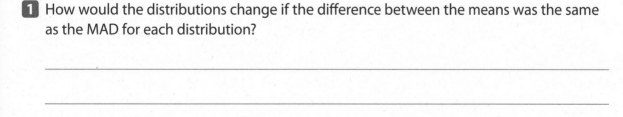

_____

_____

_____

Learn About Comparing Variabilities and Centers

Read the problem below. Then explore ways to compare data sets that have similar variabilities but different centers.

> Many of the basketball players at Chesapeake State had graduated from Central Middle School. The heights, in inches, of the players on the boys' team at Central Middle School are listed below. How can Marcus compare the heights of players on the boys' team at Central Middle School to those on the men's team at Chesapeake State?
>
> 69, 63, 62, 62, 67, 60, 61, 67, 60, 67, 66, 65, 64, 66, 63

▶ **Model It** You can compare the dot plots for each distribution.

The mean height of the men's team is 77.2 inches. Using the data for the boys' team, you can find the mean to the nearest tenth of an inch:

$$\frac{60 + 60 + 61 + 62 + 62 + 63 + 63 + 64 + 65 + 66 + 66 + 67 + 67 + 67 + 69}{15} \approx 64.1$$

You can use vertical segments to mark the mean for each data set.

Players' Heights

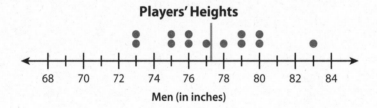

Men (in inches)

Players' Heights

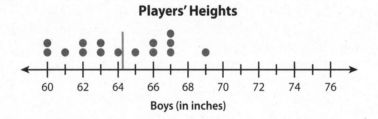

Boys (in inches)

Connect It Now you will use these representations to compare the data sets.

2 What is the difference between the mean height for men on the Chesapeake State team and the mean height for boys on the middle school team? _____

3 Compute the mean absolute deviation for boys' height, to the nearest tenth. How does it compare to 2.4, the mean absolute deviation for men's height?

_____

_____

4 By what number would you have to multiply the MAD of the boys' heights to get the difference between the mean heights you found in problem 2? Round your answer to the nearest tenth.

_____

5 What would the dot plot look like if you combined the data from boys at Central Middle School with the data from men at Chesapeake State to make one big dot plot?

_____

6 You would have to multiply the MAD by more than 3 to get the difference between the means in these distributions. When the means of distributions are more than 3 MADs apart, do you expect them to have a lot of values in common? Why or why not?

_____

_____

Try It Use what you just learned about comparing distributions to solve this problem. Show your work on a separate sheet of paper.

7 The Central Middle School girls' basketball team has a mean height of 62.3 inches, and a MAD of 2.3 (the same MAD as the Chesapeake University women's team). How many MADs greater is the mean height for the Chesapeake University women's team? (Remember: the mean height for the women was 71.5 inches).

_____

_____

Practice ▸ **Comparing Variabilities and Centers**

Read the example below. Then solve problems 8–10.

Example

Sara was curious about how many text messages students with cell phones send each day. She surveyed a random sample of students who own cell phones at the middle school and another at the high school. For the middle school data set, the mean number of texts per day was 60. For the high school data set, the mean number was 76. The MADs for the data sets were the same. Both MADs were 5.

How does the difference of the means compare to the mean absolute deviations?

Look at how you can use the information in the problem to answer the question.

The difference in the means is 16.

$16 \div 5 = 3.2$

Solution ___The difference of the means is a little more than 3 times___

___the mean absolute deviations.___

 The student divided the difference in the means by the mean absolute deviation to solve the problem.

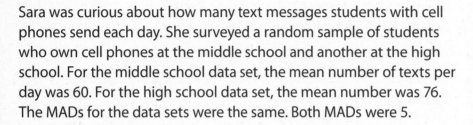 **Pair/Share**
Why is it good to compare data sets using MADs along with looking at the differences between the means of the data sets?

---

8 How would the dot plots of the data described in the student model differ? How might they be the same? Explain.

Show your work.

 What does it mean when the MADs of two sets of data are about the same?

Solution _____

_____

 Pair/Share
What are some kinds of data sets that you might want to compare that would NOT have similar MADs?

9 Do you think that the two data sets described on the previous page have a lot of values in common? Why or why not?

Show your work.

Solution _____

_____

_____

10 Which pair of data sets is most likely to have the greatest number of values in common?

A Data set 1: mean = 7
Data set 2: mean = 15;
MAD for both data sets is 8

B Data set 1: mean = 7
Data set 2: mean = 15
MAD for both data sets is 4

C Data set 1: mean = 10
Data set 2: mean = 18
MAD for both data sets is 2

D Data set 1: mean = 10
Data set 2: mean = 15
MAD for both data sets is 1

Bryce chose **D** as the correct answer. How did he get that answer?

_____

_____

_____

_____

_____

_____

Practice ▶ **Comparing Variabilities and Centers**

Solve the problems.

1 The mean absolute deviation is best described as:

A The value obtained when you add all the values in a data set and divide by the number of values.

B The value obtained when averaging the distances between each data point in a distribution and the mean.

C The difference between the means of two similar distributions.

D An approximation of the center of a statistical distribution.

2 Average winter temperatures in 45 states were recorded and divided by geographic region. Choose *True* or *False* for each statement below.

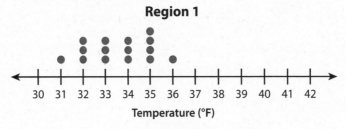

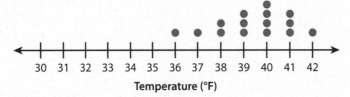

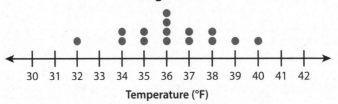

a. The mean of Region 2 is 5.8 greater than the mean of Region 1. ☐ True ☐ False

b. The data of Region 2 has greater variability than the data of Region 3 because the data are clustered around a greater average temperature. ☐ True ☐ False

c. The difference of the means of Region 2 and Region 3 is about twice the MAD of Region 3. ☐ True ☐ False

d. The average of the means of the three regions is closest to the mean of Region 3. ☐ True ☐ False

3 Mr. Douglas trains a group of student athletes. He wants to know how they are improving in the number of sit-ups they can do. The following dot plots show the number of sit-ups each student was able to do last month and this month.

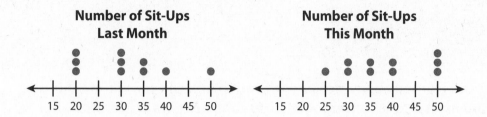

By how much did the mean number of sit-ups increase from last month to this month?

4 Make up two data sets. List all the values in each data set and write a story to describe where they may have originated. The data sets should meet the following conditions:

- The means should be different.

- The MADs should be similar.

- The means should be more than one MAD apart.

Be sure to show work to demonstrate that your data sets meet the above conditions.

✓ **Self Check**   **Go back and see what you can check off on the Self Check on page 247.**

Lesson 29 Introduction
Using Measures of Center and Variability to Compare Data

Use What You Know

In Lesson 28 you learned about measures of variability. You can use measures of variability and measures of center together to compare data distributions.

Each day during the month of September, an inspector at the Super Charge battery factory took a random sample of 30 AA batteries from the assembly line. Across the street at the Long Life battery factory, their inspector did the same thing. Each inspector placed the batteries in a flashlight and recorded how many hours they lasted. The dots in the dot plots below indicate the average life for batteries in each sample.

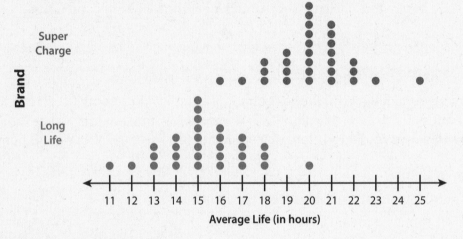

Use the dot plots to compare the data.

Use the math you already know to solve the problem.

a. Describe the center of each battery life distribution.

_____

_____

b. Describe the spread of each battery life distribution. _____

_____

c. Based on this information, if Long Life and Super Charge batteries both cost the same

amount, which brand would you buy? Why? _____

_____

One way to compare distributions to one another is to locate the center of each. The distributions for Long Life and Super Charge have middle values where the data tend to cluster. Means computed from random samples of a population tend to cluster like this.

After looking at a dot plot to see if there is a central cluster, it can be helpful to compute a measure of center such as the median, and to create a box plot. The box plot below shows that the median for the Long Life distribution is 15. You can make a box plot to show the median for the Super Charge distribution is 20.

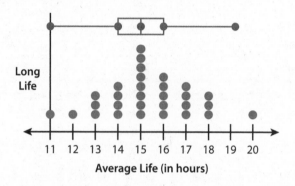

Since the median values fall within the central clusters, they do a good job of representing the typical values for each distribution. The difference in centers suggests that Super Charge is the longer-lasting brand.

Sometimes we also want to know how spread out a data set is (its variability). The smaller the spread, the more alike the battery lives are. One formal measure of variability is the interquartile range (IQR). In a box plot, it's the distance from the first to the third quartile. The interquartile range for each battery brand in our example is 2. This tells us that the middle 50% of the data lie within 2 units of one another. So, we can expect the same amount of consistency from each brand.

▶ **Reflect**

1 Compute the means for the Super Charge and Long Life distributions. Is the mean a good number for describing the center of each distribution? Why or why not?

_____

_____

_____

_____

_____

Learn About > **Comparing Data Sets**

Read the problem below. Then explore more about how to compare data sets by using measures of center and variability.

> Long Life battery factory went out of business because it lost too many customers to Super Charge. But now Super Charge has a new competitor called Power-To-Go. In the month of November, the inspector from Super Charge once again tested a random sample of 30 batteries from the assembly line each day, just as in September. The inspector from Power-To-Go did the same thing. How can consumers use statistical graphs to compare results?

▶ **Model It** **Dot plots stacked on top of one another can be used to compare the two distributions.**

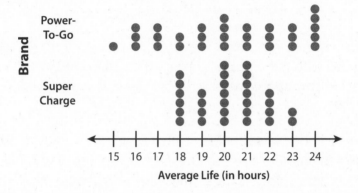

The dot plots can be used to spot central clusters, gaps, and the spread of each distribution. These characteristics can help us see important similarities and differences between the distributions. Seeing the individual values also allows us to compute the mean and MAD for each distribution.

▶ **Model It** **Box plots next to one another can also be used to compare distributions.**

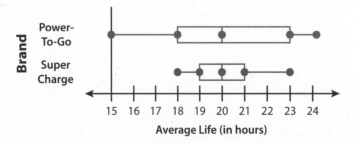

Box plots summarize the centers and spreads of the distributions.

Connect It   Now you will use these representations to compare the data sets.

2 Describe the shape, center, and spread of each distribution.

_____

_____

3 What does the box plot tell you about the distributions that the dot plot doesn't? What does the box plot not tell you about the distributions?

_____

_____

4 Which brand seems to be more consistent in its performance? Explain your reasoning.

_____

_____

5 Which battery seems to last longer? Explain your reasoning.

_____

_____

6 If you had to purchase either Super Charge or Power-To-Go batteries at a store, and they were both the same price, which one would you buy? Why?

_____

_____

Try It   Use what you just learned about comparing distributions to solve this problem.

7 Explain why it is important to look at measures of spread, and not just center, when comparing two distributions.

_____

_____

_____

Practice ▶ **Comparing Data Sets**

Read the example below. Then solve problems 8–9.

Example

Power-To-Go batteries also went out of business because of too much competition from Super Charge. A new competitor called High Energy started to make batteries. They tested samples of batteries exactly the same way as Super Charge, Long Life, and Power-To-Go. These graphs show how the High Energy sample compared to the Super Charge sample in the month of April.

The student used the box plot to determine the median and the dot plot to find the mean for each brand.

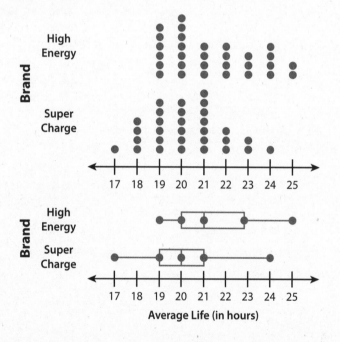

What do the mean and median tell you about each brand?

Pair/Share
Why is the mean for a data set sometimes greater than the median?

Solution _The box plot tells me that the median for Super Charge is 20 and the median for High Energy is 21. Using the values in the dot plot, you can find that the mean for Super Charge is 606 ÷ 30, or 20.2, and for High Energy it is 641 ÷ 30, or 21.4. These measures show that a typical High Energy battery should last a little longer than a typical Super Charge battery._

8 Measure the variability of each brand in two different ways. What do these measures tell you about each brand?

What are some ways to measure variability?

Solution _____

_____

_____

_____

_____

Pair/Share
If there is just one really large value in a data set, is the range a good way or a bad way to measure variability?

---

9 Suppose Super Charge and High Energy batteries are the same price. Which of the following choices is NOT a reasonable basis for making a decision about which brand to buy?

A I would buy High Energy batteries because the greater interquartile range shows that the typical High Energy battery lasts longer.

B I would buy High Energy batteries because the mean of the distribution indicates that a typical High Energy battery lasts longer.

C I would buy High Energy batteries because the median of the distribution indicates that a typical High Energy battery lasts longer.

D I would buy High Energy batteries because the data show a greater mean and a smaller range.

Angelica chose **C** as the correct answer. How did she get that answer?

What do the interquartile range, mean, and mode tell me about these two brands of batteries?

_____

_____

_____

_____

Pair/Share
How would you help Angelica understand her error?

Practice ▶ Comparing Data Sets

Solve the problems.

1 Choose the best description of how the data sets shown below compare to one another.

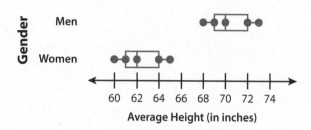

A They have similar centers and different variabilities.

B They have similar variabilities and different centers.

C The centers and variabilities are similar.

D They have different centers and different variabilities.

2 The weights of trout were randomly sampled from two different lakes. The data are presented in the histograms.

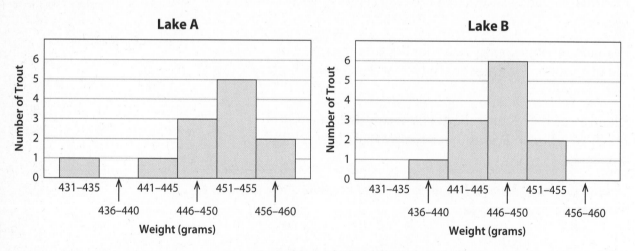

Which is a valid inference based on the histograms above? Select all that apply.

A The data from Lake A are more variable than the data from Lake B.

B The range of the data from Lake B is greater than the range of the data from Lake A.

C The weights of trout in Lake B tend to be lower than the weights of trout in Lake A.

D Differences in food supply account for the differences between the weights recorded from Lake A and the weights recorded from Lake B.

3 An unmarked sample was taken from one of the two lakes in problem 2, and the results are shown in the dot plot.

Trout Weights

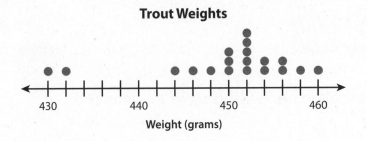

Weight (grams)

This sample is more likely from which lake, Lake A or Lake B? _____

4 Make up two data sets. List all the values in each data set and write a story to describe where they may have come from. The data sets should meet the following conditions:

- The data should come from random samples taken from a population.

- The centers of the distributions should be similar.

- The variabilities of the distributions should be different.

Be sure to show the work to demonstrate that your data sets meet the above conditions.

✓ Self Check Go back and see what you can check off on the Self Check on page 247.

Think It Through

How can you describe the likelihood of an event?

A **probability** describes the likelihood of an event happening.

An **outcome** is one of the possible results of an experiment. An **event** is a set of one or more outcomes.

Consider the **experiment** of rolling a number cube such as the one shown at the right. Each side of the number cube is labeled with a number from 1 through 6. Each of the numbers 1, 2, 3, 4, 5, and 6 is a possible outcome of the experiment.

Think How can you describe probabilities in words?

When an event will definitely happen, the probability of the event is said to be *certain*.

When an event will definitely not happen, the probability of the event is said to be *impossible*.

Other ways to describe probabilities using words include *more likely than not*, *as likely as not*, and *unlikely*.

For the number cube experiment, you can describe the probabilities of various events using words.

> **Next** to each event in the table, write the numbers that are possible outcomes.

Event		Probability
number less than 10		certain
number 7		impossible
even number		as likely as not
factor of 12		more likely than not
number 5 or 6		unlikely

When the event includes more than one possible outcome, you consider all outcomes together. For example, the event "number 5 or 6" includes two outcomes—rolling the number 5 and the number 6.

How can you describe probabilities using numbers?

Numbers between 0 and 1 describe probabilities.

Look at the diagram below. It shows how the words used to describe probabilities relate to numbers used to describe probabilities.

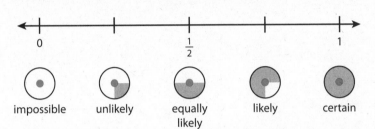

Events are more likely as their probabilities get closer to 1. Events are less likely as their probabilities get closer to 0.

When an event is impossible, the event has a probability of 0.

When an event is as likely as not, or equally likely, the event has a probability of $\frac{1}{2}$.

When an event is certain, the event has a probability of 1.

Events with probabilities between 0 and $\frac{1}{2}$ are unlikely.

Events with probabilities between $\frac{1}{2}$ and 1 are more likely than not, or likely.

▶ **Reflect**

1 The names Jessica, Joshua, Jill, and Jimmy are written on slips of paper. The slips of paper are placed in a bag. One name is picked. Name an event that is impossible. Name an event that is certain. Name an event that is as likely as not. Name an event that is more likely than not.

_____

_____

_____

_____

Think About ▷ **Understanding Probability**

🔍 **Let's Explore the Idea** Looking at the different events in an experiment will help you understand probability concepts.

2 Consider the experiment below.

A bag has 24 marbles: 6 green, 6 red, and 12 blue. Lucy reaches in the bag and picks out 1 marble.

What is the total number of marbles? _____

What is half the total number of marbles? _____

Name an event that is impossible. _____

Name an event that is certain. _____

Name an event that is as likely as not. _____

Name an event that is more likely than not. _____

Name an event that is unlikely. _____

You can show the probabilities on a number line.

3 Place each event in the correct place on the number line based on the probability of the event. Draw a line from each box to the appropriate point.

| choosing a purple marble | choosing a marble | choosing a blue marble | choosing a green marble | choosing a blue or red marble |

0          $\frac{1}{2}$ 1

Let's Talk About It Answer the questions below as a group.

4 Look at the experiment in problem 2. Explain the events you chose for *more likely than not* and *unlikely*.

_____

_____

_____

_____

5 Imagine that these cards are face down, and you pick one.

| A | A | A | B | B | C |

Name an event that has a probability of 0. _____

Name an event that has a probability of 1. _____

Name an event that has a probability of $\frac{1}{2}$. _____

Name an event that has a probability between 0 and $\frac{1}{2}$. _____

Name an event that has a probability between $\frac{1}{2}$ and 1. _____

Try It Another Way Work with your group to write a word describing the probability of each event.

6 Experiment: Spin the spinner.
Event: spinning a vowel

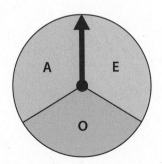

7 Experiment: Toss a penny on the mat with penny-sized circles.
Event: penny touches a circle

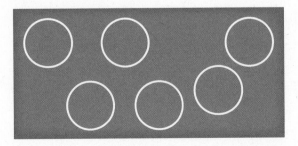

_____   _____

Connect **Understanding Probability**

Talk through these problems as a class, then write your answers below.

8 Compare A meteorologist in Seattle says there is a 75% chance of rain. A meteorologist in Tacoma says there is a $\frac{1}{4}$ chance of rain. In which city is it more likely to rain? Explain your answer.

_____

_____

_____

9 Explain Kelly said that because there are four equal-sized sections on the spinner below, the probability of the spinner landing on X is as likely as not.

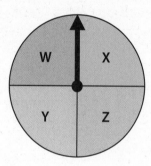

Explain why Kelly is wrong.

_____

_____

_____

10 Translate Describe each probability in words.

0 _____

$\frac{7}{8}$ _____

$\frac{1}{3}$ _____

1 _____

$\frac{1}{2}$ _____

Apply ▶ Understanding Probability

11 Put It Together Use what you have learned to complete this task.

Part A Construct a spinner with the following characteristics:

It is certain to land on blue, yellow, green, or red.

It is twice as likely to land on red than green.

It is equally likely to land on blue or green.

It is more likely to land on yellow than not land on yellow.

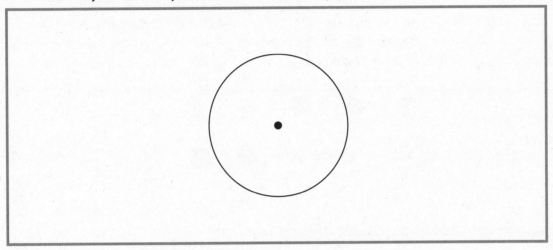

Part B Based on your spinner, identify some fractions that could possibly describe the probability of landing on each color. Justify your answer.

_____

_____

_____

_____

_____

_____

_____

_____

Ⓖ Use What You Know

In Lesson 30, you learned about probability concepts. Consider this problem.

Jada has a bag with tiles. She pulls a tile from the bag without looking, records the shape, and then puts the tile back in the bag. She gets a star 5 times, a circle 3 times, and a square 2 times. Suppose Jada does the same experiment 100 times. What is a reasonable prediction for the number of times she will pull a tile with a star? a circle? a square?

Use the math you already know to solve the problem.

a. How many times did Jada pull a tile out of the bag? _____

b. How many tiles did Jada pull that have a star on them? _____

c. Write a fraction to represent the fraction of tiles that are stars. _____

d. Write a fraction to represent the fraction of tiles that are circles. _____

e. Write a fraction to represent the fraction of tiles that are squares. _____

f. If Jada pulls 100 tiles out of the bag, would you expect there to be more tiles with stars or more tiles with squares? Explain your reasoning.

_____

_____

g. Jada pulls 100 tiles out of the bag. How could you predict how many tiles you expect to be stars? circles? squares? Explain your reasoning.

_____

_____

_____

When you find the likelihood that an event will occur, you are finding the probability of the event. Each time Jada pulls a tile from the bag, she is conducting an experiment. In probability, the experiment is a **trial**. The result of the trial is an **outcome**.

Jada pulled a tile out of the bag 10 times, so she completed 10 trials.

The outcome of each trial was a star, a circle, or a square.

You can use the notation P(outcome) to represent the probability of getting an outcome. For example, write P(star) to represent the probability of pulling a tile with a star on it.

You can find the **experimental probability** of pulling each shape from the bag based on the outcomes of Jada's experiment and the number of trials.

P(star)	P(circle)	P(square)
$\dfrac{\text{number of stars}}{\text{number of trials}} = \dfrac{5}{10}$	$\dfrac{\text{number of circles}}{\text{number of trials}} = \dfrac{3}{10}$	$\dfrac{\text{number of squares}}{\text{number of trials}} = \dfrac{2}{10}$

Each probability is based on the results from Jada's experiment. If Jada repeats the experiment, she would likely again pull more stars than circles or squares. She may get a different number of stars, circles, and squares, but over a large number of trials, you would expect the ratio of stars in the samples to reflect the ratio of stars in the population. You can use this proportional relationship to predict the number of stars, circles, and squares if Jada pulls 100 tiles from the bag.

$$\frac{\text{number of outcomes (10 trials)}}{\text{number of trials (10 trials)}} = \frac{\text{number of outcomes (100 trials)}}{\text{number of trials (100 trials)}}$$

Number of Stars	Number of Circles	Number of Squares
$\dfrac{5}{10} = \dfrac{s}{100}$	$\dfrac{3}{10} = \dfrac{c}{100}$	$\dfrac{2}{10} = \dfrac{q}{100}$
$\dfrac{5 \times 10}{10 \times 10} = \dfrac{50}{100}$	$\dfrac{3 \times 10}{10 \times 10} = \dfrac{30}{100}$	$\dfrac{2 \times 10}{10 \times 10} = \dfrac{20}{100}$

Based on Jada's initial experiment, if she does the experiment 100 times she should expect to pull out about 50 stars, 30 circles, and 20 squares.

▶ **Reflect** **Jada repeats the experiment 100 times. Do you think her results will exactly match your predictions? Explain.**

_____

_____

Learn About **Finding Experimental Probabilities**

Read the problem below. Then explore different ways to understand experimental probability.

Luke rolls a number cube and records his results in the frequency table below.

Number Rolled	Tally	Number of Times Rolled
1	I	1
2	I	1
3	IIII	4
4		0
5	II	2
6	II	2

Based on these results, what is the probability of rolling a 1? 2? 3? 4? 5? 6?

▶ **Picture It** **You can use a line plot to display the results of the experiment.**

The line plot makes it easy to compare how many times each number was rolled.

Luke's Number Cube Experiment

```
                x
                x
                x           x       x
    x   x   x           x       x
    ←---+---+---+---+---+---+---→
        1   2   3   4   5   6
          Number of Times Rolled
```

▶ **Model It** **Write each experimental probability in words.**

$P(\text{rolling a 1}) = \dfrac{\text{number of 1s rolled}}{\text{number of rolls}}$ $P(\text{rolling a 4}) = \dfrac{\text{number of 4s rolled}}{\text{number of rolls}}$

$P(\text{rolling a 2}) = \dfrac{\text{number of 2s rolled}}{\text{number of rolls}}$ $P(\text{rolling a 5}) = \dfrac{\text{number of 5s rolled}}{\text{number of rolls}}$

$P(\text{rolling a 3}) = \dfrac{\text{number of 3s rolled}}{\text{number of rolls}}$ $P(\text{rolling a 6}) = \dfrac{\text{number of 6s rolled}}{\text{number of rolls}}$

Connect It Now you will solve the problem from the previous page using ratios to write the probabilities based on the experiment.

2 Look at the tally chart on the previous page. How many times did Luke roll the number cube? _____

3 Based on Luke's experiment, find the probabilities of rolling each number.

$P(1)$ 5 _____ $P(4)$ 5 _____

$P(2)$ 5 _____ $P(5)$ 5 _____

$P(3)$ 5 _____ $P(6)$ 5 _____

4 Use a number cube and perform Luke's experiment. Record your results in the frequency table at the right. Write the probability of rolling each number in the last column.

Number	Tally	Rolls	Probability
1			$P(1) =$
2			$P(2) =$
3			$P(3) =$
4			$P(4) =$
5			$P(5) =$
6			$P(6) =$

5 Compare the probabilities from your experiment to Luke's results. Are your results different than Luke's? Explain.

_____

_____

Try It Use what you learned to solve this problem. Show your work on a separate sheet of paper.

A spinner is divided into 5 equal-sized sections, lettered A to E. Kyle spins the pointer on the spinner 25 times. He records his results in the frequency table shown at the right.

Letter	Tally	Number of Spins
A	卌I	6
B	卌	5
C	卌II	7
D	IIII	4
E	III	3

6 Based on these results, what is the probability the pointer lands on the letter D? _____

7 What is the probability the pointer lands on a vowel? _____

Learn About ▶ Making Predictions Using Proportions

Read the problem below. Then explore different ways to understand using proportions to make predictions.

Students in Luke's class combined the results of their experiments rolling a number cube. The results are shown in the table at the right.

If the class repeats the experiment for a total of 1,000 trials, predict how many times each number will occur.

Number	Number of Rolls
1	32
2	33
3	34
4	32
5	34
6	35

▶ **Picture It** Use a line plot to show the data.

Class Results of Number Cube Experiment

Number of Rolls

▶ **Model It** Find the probability of rolling each number using the class data.

Add the frequencies to find the total number of trials in the combined experiments.

$32 + 33 + 34 + 32 + 34 + 35 = 200$

$P(1) = \dfrac{\text{number of 1s rolled}}{\text{number of rolls}} = \dfrac{32}{200}$

$P(2) = \dfrac{\text{number of 2s rolled}}{\text{number of rolls}} = \dfrac{33}{200}$

$P(3) = \dfrac{\text{number of 3s rolled}}{\text{number of rolls}} = \dfrac{34}{200}$

$P(4) = \dfrac{\text{number of 4s rolled}}{\text{number of rolls}} = \dfrac{32}{200}$

$P(5) = \dfrac{\text{number of 5s rolled}}{\text{number of rolls}} = \dfrac{34}{200}$

$P(6) = \dfrac{\text{number of 6s rolled}}{\text{number of rolls}} = \dfrac{35}{200}$

Connect It Now you will solve the problem from the previous page by solving proportions to make predictions based on the results of the experiment.

8 Use Luke's class data to write and solve a proportion to predict the results for the number of 1s rolled in 1,000 rolls. _____

9 Describe the method you used to solve the proportion you wrote.

_____

_____

10 Use the results from Luke's class to write and solve proportions to predict the results for the other numbers in 1,000 trials.

2s _____   5s _____

3s _____   6s _____

4s _____

11 The class repeats the experiment with a total of only 25 trials. Predict how many times the number 4 will be rolled. Explain how you found your answer.

_____

_____

Try It Use what you learned to solve this problem. Show your work on a separate sheet of paper.

Another class rolled a number cube 100 times. The results of the experiment are shown.

12 The class repeats the experiment for a total of 1,000 trials. Predict how many times the number 4 will occur. _____

13 Predict how many times an odd number will occur in 10,000 trials. _____

Number	Number of Rolls
1	15
2	16
3	17
4	20
5	15
6	17

Practice ▶ Using Experimental Probability

Study the example below. Then solve problems 14–16.

Example

Alex randomly pulls a colored block from a bag. He records the color and then puts the block back into the bag. The table shows the results of his experiment. If he does the experiment 50 times, predict the number of times he will pull a red block from the bag.

Color	Number of Pulls
Blue	3
Red	4
Yellow	6
Green	7

Look at how you could set up a proportion to make the prediction.

Find the total number of trials in Alex's experiment.

$3 + 4 + 6 + 7 = 20$

$P(\text{red}) = \dfrac{\text{number of red blocks}}{\text{total number of trials}} = \dfrac{4}{20}$

$\dfrac{4}{20} = \dfrac{n}{50}$

$\dfrac{10}{50} = \dfrac{n}{50}$ Rewrite $\dfrac{4}{20}$ as a fraction with a denominator of 50.

$10 = n$

Solution Alex will pull a red block about 10 times.

 The student has to use Alex's results to find the probability of pulling a red block.

💬 **Pair/Share**
Would you get the same prediction if you wrote the probability as $\frac{1}{5}$ instead of $\frac{4}{20}$? Why or why not?

---

14 A spinner has a sun, a moon, and a star section. Cambria records her results from her spins in the table shown. Based on these results, predict how many times the pointer will land on the moon in 500 spins.

Show your work.

Shape	Number of Spins
Sun	11
Moon	18
Star	31

 How can you find the number you need to write an equivalent fraction?

💬 **Pair/Share**
What's another way you could answer the question?

Solution _____

15 The owner of a deli recorded the number of customers who ordered each of four sandwiches available. If the deli has 50 customers the first hour it is open, predict how many customers will order turkey sandwiches.

Show your work.

Sandwich	Number of Customers
Ham	160
Cheese	100
Turkey	180
Veggie	60

What do I need to do first?

Pair/Share
Is the answer going to be more or less than 180? Explain your reasoning.

Solution _____

---

16 Ryan has a bag with marbles. He selects a marble without looking, records the color, and then puts the marble back in the bag. In 25 trials, he selects a green marble 10 times. He selects a blue marble the other times. Based on his results, which is the best prediction of how many times Ryan will select a blue marble in 100 trials? Circle the letter of the correct answer.

A 35

B 40

C 50

D 60

How do I figure out how to find the probability that Ryan selects a blue marble?

Ryan chose **B** as the correct answer. How did Ryan get his answer?

_____

_____

_____

_____

Pair/Share
What methods could you use to predict how many blue marbles will be chosen in 100 trials?

Practice ▶ **Using Experimental Probability**

Solve the problems.

1 In the cafeteria, there are 7 teachers, 48 girls, and 45 boys. What is the probability that a person chosen at random from the cafeteria is a boy?

A $\frac{9}{20}$

C $\frac{9}{11}$

B $\frac{11}{20}$

D $\frac{1}{3}$

2 Students in a math class were divided into three groups. Each group was given a paper bag filled with an unknown number of marbles of unknown colors. For each bag, a marble was drawn at random and then put back. Each group repeated this procedure until they recorded 50 draws from the bag. The data for the three bags is shown below.

BAG A		BAG B		BAG C	
Color	**Number of Marbles**	**Color**	**Number of Marbles**	**Color**	**Number of Marbles**
Red	39	Red	10	Red	3
White	2	White	15	White	15
Yellow	9	Yellow	15	Yellow	7
Purple	0	Purple	10	Purple	25

Choose *True* or *False* for each statement.

a. In Bag B, it appears to be equally likely to draw a white marble as it is a yellow marble. ☐ True ☐ False

b. The probability of drawing a yellow marble from Bag C is approximately 7%. ☐ True ☐ False

c. The probability of drawing a purple marble from Bag A after 200 draws is likely 0. ☐ True ☐ False

d. If marbles from Bag C were drawn 10,000 times, about 600 red marbles are likely to be drawn. ☐ True ☐ False

e. Each bag definitely contains an equal number of marbles. ☐ True ☐ False

3 Students spin a spinner 500 times. The table shows the results of their experiment.

Color	Number of Spins
Purple	100
White	200
Blue	150
Pink	50

Based on these results, predict the number of times the spinner will land on blue in 100 spins.

The pointer will land on blue _____ times.

4 Tiles with the letters from Ron's name are in a bag. Ron draws a tile at random, records the letter in a table, and then replaces the letter back in the bag. The table shows the results of his experiment. Predict the number of times Ron will select a consonant in 10,000 trials.

Letter	Number of Draws
R	31
O	28
N	41

Show your work.

Answer Ron will select a consonant about _____ times.

5 Mindie tosses a coin 50 times and gets 32 heads. Adam tosses the same coin 50 times and gets 28 heads. Cam tosses the coin 50 times and gets 21 heads. Jade tosses the coin 50 times and gets 24 heads. Use the results to predict the number of heads in 1,000 tosses.

Show your work.

Answer There will be about _____ heads in 1,000 tosses.

 **Self Check** Go back and see what you can check off on the Self Check on page 247.

↻ Use What You Know

In Lesson 31, you learned about probability based on an experiment. Consider this problem.

A game at a school carnival has three different spinners. The spinners are shown. Which spinner is most likely to land on section A?

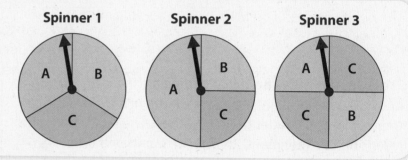

Spinner 1   Spinner 2   Spinner 3

Use the math you already know to solve the problem.

a. How can you set up a ratio to represent section A on Spinner 1? What fraction of Spinner 1 is represented by section A?

_____

b. Is the pointer on Spinner 1 more likely to land on section A than on B or C? Explain.

_____

c. What fraction of Spinner 2 is represented by section A? _____

d. Is the pointer on Spinner 2 more likely to land on section A than on B or C? Explain.

_____

e. Which section is Spinner 3 most likely to land on? Explain. _____

_____

f. Explain how to use ratios to decide which spinner is most likely to land on section A.

_____

_____

When you find the probability of an event based on the results from an experiment, you are finding the **experimental probability** of that event. The probabilities you found in Lesson 31 are experimental probabilities.

$$\text{experimental probability of an event} = \frac{\text{number of times event occurs}}{\text{number of trials}}$$

The **theoretical probability** of an event is what you would expect to happen in an experiment. You can use theoretical probability to find the likelihood of an event.

The **sample space** is the set of all possible outcomes for an experiment. For all of the spinners, the sample space is the set of letters A, B, and C. When the probability model is **uniform**, where each outcome is equally likely, you can use the following ratio:

$$\text{theoretical probability of an event} = \frac{\text{number of favorable outcomes}}{\text{total number of outcomes}}$$

For Spinner 1, each outcome is equally likely, so that probability model is uniform.

The favorable outcome is the letter of interest. The number of outcomes is the number of different letters on each spinner.

For example: $P(C \text{ on Spinner 1}) = \frac{\text{letter C}}{\text{number of different letters}} = \frac{1}{3}$

On Spinner 2, A covers more of the spinner than B or C. On Spinner 3, C covers more of the spinner than A or B. The outcomes A, B, and C, are not equally likely for Spinners 2 and 3. These probability models are **non-uniform**. For these spinners, consider how much of the spinner is covered by the favorable outcome to find the theoretical probability.

On Spinner 2, A covers $\frac{1}{2}$ of the spinner, so $P(A \text{ on Spinner 2}) = \frac{1}{2}$.

On Spinner 3, C also covers $\frac{1}{2}$ of the spinner, so $P(C \text{ on Spinner 3}) = \frac{1}{2}$.

Which spinner is most likely to land on A? Find each theoretical probability.

$P(A \text{ on Spinner 1}) = \frac{1}{3}$ $\qquad$ $P(A \text{ on Spinner 2}) = \frac{1}{2}$ $\qquad$ $P(A \text{ on Spinner 3}) = \frac{1}{4}$

One-half is greater than $\frac{1}{3}$ or $\frac{1}{4}$. Spinner 2 is most likely to land on A.

▶ **Reflect**

1 Which spinner is more likely than the others to land on B? Explain.

_____

_____

Learn About 〉 **Using a Probability Model**

Read the problem below. Then explore different ways to understand it.

A family has three girls. The family tossed a coin to represent the likelihood of a girl if they have another child. They let heads represent a girl and tails represent a boy. The table shows the results of their experiment.

Coin Toss	Tally	Total
Heads (Girl)	⅟⅟⅟⅟ |||	8
Tails (Boy)	⅟⅟⅟⅟ ⅟⅟⅟⅟ ||	12

If the family has another child, predict whether the child will be a girl.

▶ **Picture It** Describe the sample space.

The sample space consists of two possible equally likely outcomes: girl or boy.

The favorable outcome is a girl.

▶ **Model It** Compare the experimental probability to the theoretical probability.

Experimental probability of a girl:

Use the results of the experiment.

$$P(\text{Girl}) = \frac{\text{number of heads}}{\text{number of tosses}} = \frac{8}{20}$$

Theoretical probability of having a girl:

number of equally likely possible outcomes: 2 (girl or boy)

favorable outcomes: 1 (girl)

$$P(\text{Girl}) = \frac{\text{number of favorable outcomes}}{\text{total number of outcomes}} = \frac{1}{2}$$

The experimental probability of a girl is less than the theoretical probability of a girl.

Connect It Now you will solve the problem from the previous page using probability.

2 Based on the results of the family experiment, predict whether the next child will be a girl. Explain.

_____

_____

3 Repeat the experiment by tossing the coin 20 times. Record your results in the chart.

Coin Toss	Tally	Total
Heads (Girl)		
Tails (Boy)		

4 Based on your results, what is the experimental probability of a girl? _____

5 Compare the experimental probability from problem 4 to the theoretical probability of having a girl.

_____

_____

6 Will the experimental and theoretical probability of an event always differ? Why or why not?

_____

_____

Try It Use what you learned to solve this problem.

7 What is the theoretical probability that the child will be a boy? _____

8 Does the fact that the family has 3 girls change the probability that the next child is a girl? Explain.

_____

_____

Read the problem below. Then explore different ways to understand it.

Serena is playing a game with a number cube. To win the game, she must roll the number 4 on her next roll. The table shows the number of times she has rolled each number so far.

Number	Number of Rolls
1	3
2	6
3	2
4	5
5	4
6	4

What is the probability that Serena will win the game?

▶ **Picture It** **Find the theoretical probability.**

Describe the sample space.

The sample space is the set of possible numbers that can be rolled: 1, 2, 3, 4, 5, and 6.

Each outcome is equally likely.

The favorable outcome is the number Serena needs to win: the number 4.

$$P(4) = \frac{\text{number of favorable outcomes}}{\text{total number of outcomes}} = \frac{1}{6}$$

▶ **Model It** **Find the experimental probability.**

Find the total number of rolls.

$$3 + 6 + 2 + 5 + 4 + 4 = 24$$

The favorable outcome is the number of times 4 was rolled: 5 times

$$P(4) = \frac{\text{number of times 4 was rolled}}{\text{total number of rolls}} = \frac{5}{24}$$

Connect It Now you will solve the problem from the previous page using probability.

9 Repeat the experiment using a number cube. Roll the number cube 24 times. Record your results on the line plot.

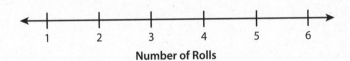

Number of Rolls

10 Based on your results, what is the experimental probability that Serena will win?

_____

11 Compare your results to the given experimental data. How are your results similar? How are they different? _____

_____

12 Combine the results of your experiment with those from your class. Record the results in the table to the right.

13 Based on the class results, what is the experimental probability that Serena will win?

_____

Number	Number of Rolls
1	
2	
3	
4	
5	
6	

Try It Use what you learned about experimental probability to answer these questions.

14 Compare the experimental probability of the combined data from your class to the theoretical probability that Serena will win. _____

_____

15 Why might the combined data be a better prediction of the probability than your results alone?

_____

_____

Learn About > Solving Problems with Experimental Probability

Read the problem below. Then explore different ways to understand it.

Rafael tosses a paper cup and records how the paper cup lands. The table shows the results of his experiment.

Paper Cup Landing	Number of Times
Sideways	16
Open-end down	4
Open-end up	0

Predict whether the paper cup will land open-end down on his next toss. Use probability to explain your prediction.

▶ **Model It** Write the experimental probability of each landing.

Find the total number of trials.

$16 + 4 + 0 = 20$

$P(\text{Sideways}) = \dfrac{\text{number of sideways landings}}{\text{number of trials}} = \dfrac{16}{20} = \dfrac{4}{5}$

$P(\text{Open-end down}) = \dfrac{\text{number of open-end down landings}}{\text{number of trials}} = \dfrac{4}{20} = \dfrac{1}{5}$

$P(\text{Open-end up}) = \dfrac{\text{number of open-end up landings}}{\text{number of trials}} = \dfrac{0}{20} = 0$

▶ **Picture It** Understand the experiment.

The paper cup lands sideways 16 times, open-end down 4 times, and never open-end up.

The paper cup never lands with the open-end up. The top of the cup is open while the bottom is closed. So, the weights of the ends are different.

The experiment does not have equally likely outcomes.

You cannot write the theoretical probability without more information.

Use the experimental probability of each landing to make the prediction.

> **Connect It** Now you will solve the problem from the previous page using probability.

16 Why does it appear that the outcomes for the experiment are not equally likely?

_____

_____

17 Use a paper cup to repeat Rafael's experiment. Record your results for 20 tosses.

Paper Cup Landing	Tally	Number of Times
Sideways		
Open-end down		
Open-end up		

18 Combine the results of your experiment with those from your class. Record the results.

Paper Cup Landing	Tally	Number of Times
Sideways		
Open-end down		
Open-end up		

19 Use the class results to find the experimental probability of each landing.

_____

20 The paper cup experiment is non-uniform. Tossing a coin is an experiment that is uniform. Describe the differences and similarities between finding the probability of how a paper cup lands to finding the probability of how a tossed coin lands.

_____

_____

> **Try It** Use what you learned to solve this problem.

21 How is predicting the paper cup results similar to the coin results? How is it different?

_____

_____

_____

Practice Solving Problems with Probability Models

Study the example below. Then solve problems 22–24.

Example

Pablo works at a pizza parlor. On average, 70% of the pizzas ordered have thick crust, and 30% have thin crust. Use the random number table below to find the experimental probability that the next pizza ordered will have thick crust.

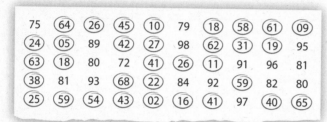

Look at how you could show your work using the random number table.

Let numbers from 00 through 69 represent ordering thick crust.
Let numbers from 70 through 99 represent ordering thin crust.
33 of the 50 numbers are numbers from 00 through 69.

Solution $\frac{33}{50}$

>
> There are many different ways to solve this problem. For example, you could let numbers from 00 through 29 represent thin crust and numbers from 30 through 99 represent thick crust.

> **Pair/Share**
> How else could you model this problem?

---

22 Of the 20 students in Kendra's class, 5 have black hair, 8 have blonde hair, 5 have brown hair, and 2 have red hair. Kendra used the spinner to find the experimental probability that this week's class leader will have blonde hair. She spun the spinner 15 times and recorded her results.

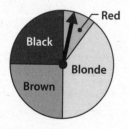

Color	Number of Times
Black	2
Blonde	9
Brown	3
Red	1

>
> What does the denominator of the fraction represent?

What is the experimental probability that this week's class leader will have blonde hair?

Show your work.

Solution _____

>
> **Pair/Share**
> Why are the sections of the spinner different sizes?

23 Staci answers a 6-question true or false quiz randomly. What is the experimental probability that Staci will correctly answer exactly half of the questions?

Each of the 6 numbers in the outcomes represents 1 quiz question.

Model the problem by rolling six number cubes at the same time. Let even numbers represent a correct answer and odd numbers represent an incorrect answer. Roll the number cubes 9 times and record your results in the table. The first trial has been done for you.

Trial	Outcomes	Trial	Outcomes	Trial	Outcomes
1	1, 5, 4, 5, 3, 3	4		7	
2		5		8	
3		6		9	

Show your work.

 Pair/Share
What can you use instead of a number cube to model this situation?

Solution _____

---

24 On average, Ava makes 80% of her free throws. In the following random number table, any number from 0 through 7 represents a make, and an 8 or 9 represents a miss. Start at the top left of the table and look at 20 consecutive number pairs as you move to the right to represent Ava's next two free throws. For example, a number pair of 09 represents making the first free throw and missing the second. Based on the model, what is the experimental probability that Ava will make her next two free throws?

Even though there's a gap between the 5th and 6th numbers, they still represent a number pair.

```
23  89  45  58  87  76  93  86  64  18  19  26  75  94  83  79  44  53  02  44
71  01  54  95  87  24  44  00  53  58  95  45  77  87  35  18  54  43  97  89
94  73  08  92  66  57  66  21  63  91  51  70  90  63  48  48  46  45  30  14
```

A $\frac{1}{2}$ **C** $\frac{13}{20}$

B $\frac{11}{20}$ **D** $\frac{4}{5}$

Bill chose **D** as the correct answer. How did Bill get that answer?

_____

_____

_____

 Pair/Share
Does Bill's answer make sense?

Practice ⟩ **Solving Problems with Probability Models**

Solve the problems.

1 One out of every three boxes of cereal has a prize in it. To find the experimental probability that the next box he buys will have a prize, Joe rolls a number cube 50 times. He lets a multiple of 3 represent a box with a prize and all other numbers represent a box without a prize. His results are shown in the table to the right. What is the experimental probability that Joe's next box will have a prize in it?

Number Rolled	Number of Times
1	8
2	6
3	13
4	4
5	12
6	7

A $\frac{13}{50}$

B $\frac{1}{3}$

C $\frac{2}{5}$

D $\frac{2}{3}$

2 Two spinners are shown. Choose *True* or *False* for each statement below.

Spinner A   **Spinner B**

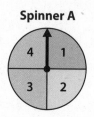 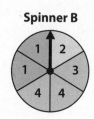

a. The probability of spinning a 1 is the same for both spinners. ☐ True ☐ False

b. The probability of spinning a 4 on Spinner B is $\frac{1}{3}$. ☐ True ☐ False

c. The probability of spinning an even number on Spinner A is $\frac{1}{2}$. ☐ True ☐ False

d. The probability of spinning a 3 on Spinner B is greater than the probability of spinning a 3 on Spinner A. ☐ True ☐ False

3 Tanya wants to know the probability that a family with 3 children has 2 boys and 1 girl. She modeled the problem by tossing three coins at the same time. She let heads represent a boy and tails represent a girl. The results of her 20 tosses are shown in the following table.

Trial	Outcome	Trial	Outcome
1	H, T, H	11	T, T, H
2	T, T, T	12	H, H, T
3	T, H, H	13	H, H, H
4	H, H, T	14	T, T, H
5	H, T, H	15	T, H, T
6	T, T, H	16	T, T, H
7	H, H, H	17	H, H, T
8	T, H, T	18	T, H, H
9	T, T, H	19	T, T, T
10	H, T, T	20	H, H, T

Part A What is the experimental probability that a family with 3 children will have 2 boys and 1 girl?

Show your work.

Answer _____

Part B The theoretical probability of 2 boys and 1 girl is $\frac{3}{8}$. How does the experimental probability above compare to the theoretical probability?

_____

_____

✓ **Self Check** **Go back and see what you can check off on the Self Check on page 247.**

↻ Use What You Know

You've learned how to list the outcomes of an event. In this lesson, you will learn how to find the probability of more than one event. Take a look at this problem.

> Two sisters, Alice and Mari, are each expecting a baby. The family wants to be surprised about the gender of the babies. What is the probability that both babies will be girls?

Use the math you already know to solve this problem.

a. If one of the babies is a girl, what are the possible outcomes of the other baby?

_____

b. If one of the babies is a boy, what are the possible outcomes of the other baby?

_____

c. Complete this table of possible outcomes.

	Mari's Baby	
Alice's Baby	**B**	**G**
B		BG
G		

d. How many possible outcomes are there? _____

e. Out of the possible outcomes, how many are two girls? _____

f. Explain how to find the probability that both babies will be girls.

_____

_____

_____

This problem asks you to find the probability of a **compound event**, or more than one event.

To solve this problem, you listed the possible outcomes and showed the sample space in a table. Another way to show the sample space is to use a **tree diagram**.

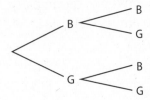

You need to know all the possible outcomes to find the probability. Two girls is 1 favorable outcome out of 4 possible outcomes, so the probability of two girls is $\frac{1}{4}$.

Reflect

1 Draw a tree diagram to show the sample space and all possible outcomes of children for a family with 4 children.

Learn About ▶ **Representing Sample Spaces and Identifying Outcomes**

Read the problem below. Then explore how to represent sample spaces and identify outcomes.

> Charlotte is playing a board game. To move her game piece, she needs to roll the same number on two number cubes. Represent the sample space and find all the ways Charlotte could roll the same number.

▶ **Model It** **You can draw a tree diagram to understand the problem.**

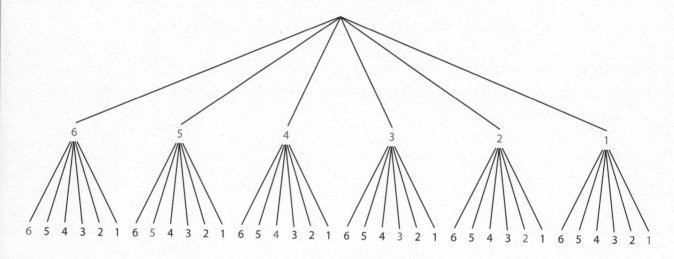

▶ **Model It** **You can make a table to understand the problem.**

1, 1	1, 2	1, 3	1, 4	1, 5	1, 6
2, 1	2, 2	2, 3	2, 4	2, 5	2, 6
3, 1	3, 2	3, 3	3, 4	3, 5	3, 6
4, 1	4, 2	4, 3	4, 4	4, 5	4, 6
5, 1	5, 2	5, 3	5, 4	5, 5	5, 6
6, 1	6, 2	6, 3	6, 4	6, 5	6, 6

Connect It Now you will solve problems using the models.

2 How does the tree diagram represent the sample space? How many outcomes are possible?

_____

_____

3 How many branches of the tree diagram represent rolling the same number on

both cubes? _____

4 Look at the table. List all the outcomes that are the same number on both cubes.

_____

5 To move his game piece, Nathan needs to roll two even numbers. Are there more or fewer favorable outcomes for Nathan than Charlotte? Explain.

_____

_____

6 Why do you need to know the total number of outcomes in a sample space?

_____

_____

Try It Use what you learned about identifying the number of times an event occurs within a sample space to solve this problem. Show your work on a separate sheet of paper.

7 Represent the sample space of tossing a coin and rolling a number cube.

    A. How many outcomes are possible? _____

    B. How many times does a head and an even number occur? _____

Learn About Finding Probabilities of Compound Events

Read the problem below. Then explore how to find probabilities of compound events.

Reese and James are playing paper, rock, scissors. What is the probability that at least one person will show rock? (Assume all outcomes are equally likely.)

▶ **Model It** **You can draw a tree diagram to understand the problem.**

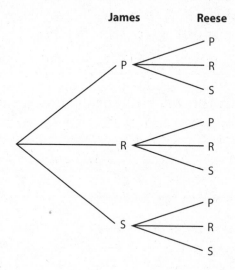

▶ **Model It** **You can make a table to understand the problem.**

James	Reese		
	Paper	**Rock**	**Scissors**
Paper	PP	PR	PS
Rock	RP	RR	RS
Scissors	SP	SR	SS

Connect It Now you will solve the problem using the models.

8 What does the sample space represent? _____

_____

9 How many possible outcomes are in the sample space? _____

10 Explain the difference between PR and RP. _____

_____

11 List all the ways that at least one rock comes up. How many such outcomes are there?

_____

12 What is the probability of at least 1 rock coming up? 2 rocks coming up? Explain.

_____

_____

13 Explain how to find the probability of compound events.

_____

_____

_____

Try It Use what you just learned about finding a compound probability to solve these problems. Show your work on a separate sheet of paper.

14 In the game, paper beats rock, scissors beat paper, and rock beats scissors.

A. List the ways in which James can win. _____

B. List the ways in which Reese can win. _____

C. If both Reese and James show the same sign, there is a tie. What is the probability of

a tie? Explain. _____

_____

Read the problem below. Then explore how to find a compound probability with more than two events.

At a smoothie stand, you can order a fruit smoothie in three different sizes: small, medium, or large. You can choose strawberries, mango, or both fruits. Then, you can choose to add yogurt or not. If all the types of smoothies are equally likely to be ordered, what is the probability that someone will order a smoothie with strawberries and yogurt in it?

▶ **Model It** You can draw a tree diagram to understand the problem.

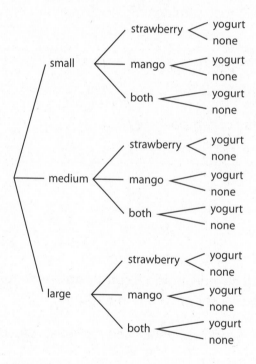

▶ **Model It** You can identify and list favorable outcomes to understand the problem.

small with strawberries & yogurt

small with both fruits & yogurt

medium with strawberries & yogurt

medium with both fruits & yogurt

large with strawberries & yogurt

large with both fruits & yogurt

Connect It Now you will solve the problem using the models.

15 What does the sample space represent? How many total outcomes are in the

sample space? _____

_____

16 Look at the list of favorable outcomes. For each size, how many smoothies have both strawberries and yogurt? Explain.

_____

17 How many outcomes have both strawberries and yogurt? _____

18 What is the probability of ordering a smoothie with strawberries and yogurt? What is the probability of an order not being a smoothie with strawberries and yogurt? Explain.

_____

_____

_____

19 Explain how knowing the probability an event will occur means you also know the probability that event will not occur?

_____

_____

Try It Use what you just learned about finding the compound probability to solve this problem. Show your work on a separate sheet of paper.

20 A sandwich shop offers a choice of white or wheat bread, three choices for meat (turkey, ham, or roast beef), and four choices for cheese (Swiss, American, cheddar, or no cheese).

A. Represent the sample space with a model. How many outcomes are possible?

_____

B. What is the probability someone will order wheat bread with either turkey or ham if the choice is at random?

_____

C. What is the probability someone will order a sandwich with no cheese if the choice is at random?

_____

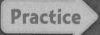
Practice > **Finding Probabilities of Compound Events**

Study the example below. Then solve problems 21–23.

Example

Harry has 4 shirts and some number of pairs of pants in his closet. He has a total of 8 possible outfits choosing one shirt and one pair of pants. How many pairs of pants are in Harry's closet?

Look at how you can show your work using a table.

I know that 4 shirts and 1 pair of pants make a total of 4 outfits.
4 shirts and 2 pair of pants make a total of 8 outfits.

| Shirt A, Pant 1 | Shirt B, Pant 1 | Shirt C, Pant 1 | Shirt D, Pant 1 |
| Shirt A, Pant 2 | Shirt B, Pant 2 | Shirt C, Pant 2 | Shirt D, Pant 2 |

Solution __There are 2 pairs of pants._____

The student used a table to think about the number of possible outcomes.

Pair/Share
How could you justify your answer with a tree diagram?

21 Sophie asks each dinner guest to select one choice from each list: main (chicken, salmon, or steak), side (potato or rice), and vegetable (beans or broccoli).

Model the sample space with all possible outcomes. Find the probability of a guest requesting either potatoes or beans if the guest chooses at random.

Show your work.

How many different outcomes are possible?

Pair/Share
What outcomes do not include potatoes or beans?

Solution _____

22 Leo and Paul each have 5 cards. Leo's cards are numbered 1, 3, 4, 5, 5. Paul's cards are numbered 1, 2, 3, 4, 6. Without looking, they each choose one card to show. The greater card wins. Make a table and list all possible outcomes. What is Leo's probability of winning? What is Paul's probability of winning?

Show your work.

Will there be ties in this game?

Solution _____

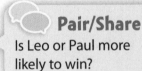

Pair/Share
Is Leo or Paul more likely to win?

23 Which of the following situations is not a compound event? Circle the letter of the correct answer.

   A   2 friends each toss a coin to call heads or tails.

   B   3 people play a game and one rolls a number cube.

   C   A family with three children has exactly 2 girls.

   D   Mike spins a spinner twice.

Sam chose **D** as the correct answer. How did he get that answer?

_____

_____

_____

Pair/Share
What should the correct answer be? Explain.

Practice ▶ **Finding Probabilities of Compound Events**

Solve the problems.

1 When rolling two number cubes, what is the probability of rolling at least one 6?

A $\frac{12}{36}$ **C** $\frac{6}{36}$

B $\frac{11}{36}$ **D** $\frac{1}{36}$

2 What is the probability that a family of 4 children has 2 boys and 2 girls?

A $\frac{4}{16}$ **C** $\frac{8}{16}$

B $\frac{6}{16}$ **D** $\frac{10}{16}$

3 Three cards, one labeled "A," one labeled "T," and one labeled "C," are picked in random order. Based on the tree diagram, which is a valid conclusion? Select all that apply.

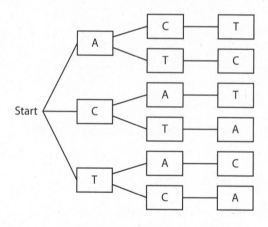

A The probability of the letters spelling CAT is $\frac{1}{6}$.

B The probability that T will be the first letter chosen is $\frac{1}{3}$.

C The probability that A will be the first letter chosen is $\frac{1}{15}$.

D The sample space consists of 6 outcomes.

E 15 cards must be drawn to determine the probability of spelling CAT.

4 A set contains the numbers 0, 6, 12, and 15. Two different numbers are selected randomly from this set. What is the probability that each event below will occur? Write a numeral in each box to form a fraction that shows your answer.

| 0 | 1 | 2 | 3 | 4 | 5 | 6 | 7 | 8 | 9 |

The probability that the sum is greater than 12 is $\dfrac{\square}{\square}$.

The probability that the product is 72 is $\dfrac{\square}{\square}$.

5 A seventh grader has 2 siblings. Model the possible orders for genders of a family with three children.

Answer There are _____ possible outcomes.

6 Use the model in problem 5 to answer these questions.

What is the probability that this seventh grader is a girl with a brother and sister?

Answer _____

What is the probability that there are at least 2 girls in the family?

Answer _____

Name an outcome with a probability of $\frac{1}{8}$.

_____

 **Self Check** **Go back and see what you can check off on the Self Check on page 247.**

Solve the problems.

1 The two dot plots record the weights of players on two professional basketball teams.

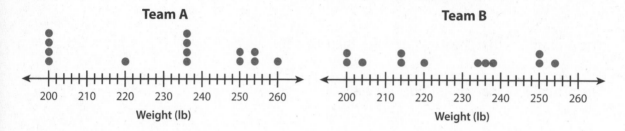

Which statement is supported by Kelly's data? Choose *True* or *False* for each statement.

a. The interquartile range (IQR) of Team A data is
15 pounds more than that of Team B data.
☐ True ☐ False

b. The mean weight of the Team A players is 5 pounds
more than the mean weight of the Team B players.
☐ True ☐ False

c. The mean absolute deviation (MAD) of the Team B
weights is greater than the MAD of the Team A weights.
☐ True ☐ False

d. The weight data for Team B is more variable than the
weight data for Team A.
☐ True ☐ False

2 If you choose a point randomly in the square, what is the probability that it is in the
circle? Write the appropriate expressions and operations that will correctly calculate the
probability, *P*, as a decimal between 0 and 1.

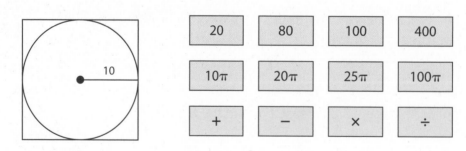

$P =$ ☐ ☐ ☐

3 Michelle tossed a quarter into the air four times.

Part A Give the sample space for all possible outcomes of tossing the quarter four times. Use H for heads and T for tails.

Part B What is the probability of getting 2 heads and 2 tails in one toss?

Answer _____

4 Blake recorded the high temperatures each day for a month in two different cities. For City A, the mean high temperature was 59°F with a mean absolute deviation of 3.2. For City B, the mean high temperature was 71°F with a mean absolute deviation of 2.9. Compare the difference of the means in terms of the mean absolute deviations.

Show your work.

Answer _____

_____

Performance Task

Answer the questions and show all your work on separate paper.

Two different juice companies are running a special promotion. Sunny OJ and Starry Juice are each offering chances to win free bottles of juice. Sunny OJ puts caps that can be used as coupons for free bottles of juice on $\frac{1}{4}$ of all bottles produced. Starry Juice puts such caps on $\frac{1}{3}$ of all bottles produced.

> **Checklist**
> **Did You . . .**
> ☐ Describe the experiment?
> ☐ Record the results?
> ☐ Compare predictions with actual results?

a. A class of 16 students examines the likelihood of buying a bottle of juice that has a coupon. They simulate buying bottles of juice to predict how many coupons they will get if every student buys 1 bottle of each brand of juice each day for 10 days.

They decide to use red and blue marbles and two paper bags labeled "Sunny OJ" and "Starry Juice." They randomly select a marble from each bag and record its color.

What do the two different colors of marbles represent? How many of each color marble should the students put in each bag? Why? How many times should they randomly pick a marble from the bag and record the color? Describe in detail how the class should perform the simulation. Predict what you think the results of the simulation will be.

b. Perform the simulation using colored marbles or other objects. Display the daily results in stacked dot plots, one for each company. State the typical daily number of winning coupons for each company. Compare the actual results with the prediction you made in Part a.

Reflect

Reflect on Mathematical Practices After you complete the task, choose one of the following questions to answer.

- **Model** Why is a dot plot a good model for recording results of the simulation?

- **Reason Mathematically** How does the simulation represent the actual juice-buying activity? Describe the relationship between the simulation and real-world activity.

Glossary

A

absolute value a number's distance from 0 on the number line.

additive inverses two numbers whose sum equals zero.

approximations numbers that are not exact but are close enough to be used when solving certain problems.

B

biased sample a sample that does not represent the whole population.

C

center a point inside a circle that is equidistant from each point on the circle.

certain the probability of an event when that specific event will definitely happen.

circumference the distance around a circle.

commission a percent of a sales amount awarded to the person making the sale.

complementary angles two angles whose measures add up to 90°.

complex fraction a fraction where the numerator is a fraction, the denominator is a fraction, or both the numerator and the denominator are fractions.

compound event an event that consists of two or more simple events.

constant of proportionality the unit rate in a proportional relationship.

cross-section a two-dimensional shape that is exposed by making a straight cut through a section of a three-dimensional figure.

D

diameter the distance across the circle through the center.

E

event a set of one or more outcomes of an experiment.

experiment a repeatable procedure involving chance that results in one or more possible outcomes.

experimental probability the probability of an event based on the results from an experiment.

G

gratuity a percent added on to the cost of a service.

I

impossible the probability of an event when that specific event will definitely not happen.

M

markup a percent added to the cost of an item to determine the selling price.

Glossary

mean the average of the numbers; the sum of the values divided by the number of values.

mean absolute deviation (MAD) the average distance of each data point from the mean.

non-uniform probability model when each outcome of a probability model is not equally likely.

outcome one of the possible results of an experiment.

percent the number of parts per 100.

percent change the ratio that compares the amount of change to the original amount.

percent decrease the percent a quantity decreases from its original amount.

percent error the ratio that describes how far an estimate is from the actual amount.

percent increase the percent a quantity increases from its original amount.

pi the ratio of the circumference to the diameter, represented by the Greek letter [π].

population the entire group considered for a survey.

probability the likelihood of an event happening.

proportional relationship the relationship among a group of ratios that are equivalent.

radius the distance from the center to any point on the circle.

random sample a sample in which every element in the population has an equal chance of being selected.

random variation a variable is subject to random variation if its value is not predictable.

repeating decimals decimals that never end and repeat the same digits over and over.

right prism a solid with two parallel bases that are polygons and lateral faces perpendicular to the bases.

sample space the set of all possible outcomes for an experiment.

scale a ratio that compares the measurements used in a scale drawing with the actual measurements.

scale drawing a drawing that shows an object with its measurements in proportion to the actual measurements of the object.

scale factor a constant of proportionality.

simple interest a percent of an amount borrowed that is paid to the lender in addition to the amount borrowed.

supplementary angles two angles whose measures add up to 180°.

tax a percent of a purchase price that is added to the purchase price and paid to a government.

terminating decimals decimals that end and whose only repeating digit is 0.

theoretical probability what is expected to happen in an experiment.

tree diagram a visual model that shows all possible outcomes of an event.

trial what an experiment is called in probability.

uniform probability model when each outcome of a probability model is equally likely.

unit rate a rate in which the first quantity is compared to 1 unit of the second quantity.

vertical angles opposite angles formed when two lines intersect; vertical angles are congruent.

Common Core State Standards Coverage by *Ready* Instruction

The chart below correlates each Common Core State Standard to the *Ready® Instruction* lesson(s) that offer(s) comprehensive instruction on that standard. Use this chart to determine which lessons your students should complete based on their mastery of each standard.

Common Core State Standards for Grade 7 Mathematical Standards	Content Emphasis	*Ready®* Lesson(s)
Ratios and Proportional Relationships		
Analyze proportional relationships and use them to solve real-world and mathematical problems.		
7.RP.A.1 Compute unit rates associated with ratios of fractions, including ratios of lengths, areas and other quantities measured in like or different units. *For example, if a person walks $\frac{1}{2}$ mile in each $\frac{1}{4}$ hour, compute the unit rate as the complex fraction $\frac{\frac{1}{2}}{\frac{1}{4}}$ miles per hour, equivalently 2 miles per hour.*	Major	9, 22
7.RP.A.2 Recognize and represent proportional relationships between quantities.	Major	10, 11
7.RP.A.2a Decide whether two quantities are in a proportional relationship, e.g., by testing for equivalent ratios in a table or graphing on a coordinate plane and observing whether the graph is a straight line through the origin.	Major	10
7.RP.A.2b Identify the constant of proportionality (unit rate) in tables, graphs, equations, diagrams, and verbal descriptions of proportional relationships.	Major	10
7.RP.A.2c Represent proportional relationships by equations. *For example, if total cost t is proportional to the number n of items purchased at a constant price p, the relationship between the total cost and the number of items can be expressed as t = pn.*	Major	11
7.RP.A.2d Explain what a point (x, y) on the graph of a proportional relationship means in terms of the situation, with special attention to the points (0, 0) and (1, r) where r is the unit rate.	Major	11
7.RP.A.3 Use proportional relationships to solve multistep ratio and percent problems. Examples: simple interest, tax, markups and markdowns, gratuities and commissions, fees, percent increase and decrease, percent error.	Major	12, 13
The Number System		
Apply and extend previous understandings of operations with fractions.		
7.NS.A.1 Apply and extend previous understandings of addition and subtraction to add and subtract rational numbers; represent addition and subtraction on a horizontal or vertical number line diagram.	Major	1, 2, 3, 7
7.NS.A.1a Describe situations in which opposite quantities combine to make 0. *For example, a hydrogen atom has 0 charge because its two constituents are oppositely charged.*	Major	1, 7

The Standards for Mathematical Practice are integrated throughout the instructional lessons.

Common Core State Standards © 2010. National Governors Association Center for Best Practices and Council of Chief State School Officers. All rights reserved.

The Number System *continued*

Apply and extend previous understandings of operations with fractions. *continued*

7.NS.A.1b	Understand $p + q$ as the number located a distance $|q|$ from p, in the positive or negative direction depending on whether q is positive or negative. Show that a number and its opposite have a sum of 0 (are additive inverses). Interpret sums of rational numbers by describing real-world contexts.	Major	1, 7
7.NS.A.1c	Understand subtraction of rational numbers as adding the additive inverse, $p - q = p + (-q)$. Show that the distance between two rational numbers on the number line is the absolute value of their difference, and apply this principle in real-world contexts.	Major	2, 7
7.NS.A.1d	Apply properties ofoperations as strategies to add and subtract rational numbers.	Major	3, 7
7.NS.A.2	Apply and extend previous understandings of multiplication and division and of fractions to multiply and divide rational numbers.	Major	4, 5, 6
7.NS.A.2a	Understand that multiplication is extended from fractions to rational numbers by requiring that operations continue to satisfy the properties of operations, particularly the distributive property, leading to products such as $(-1)(-1) = 1$ and the rules for multiplying signed numbers. Interpret products of rational numbers by describing real-world contexts.	Major	4, 6
7.NS.A.2b	Understand that integers can be divided, provided that the divisor is not zero, and every quotient of integers (with non-zero divisor) is a rational number. If p and q are integers, then $-\left(\frac{p}{q}\right) = \frac{(2p)}{q} = \frac{p}{(2q)}$. Interpret quotients of rational numbers by describing real-world contexts.	Major	4, 6
7.NS.A.2c	Apply properties of operations as strategies to multiply and divide rational numbers.	Major	4, 6
7.NS.A.2d	Convert a rational number to a decimal using long division; know that the decimal form of a rational number terminates in 0s or eventually repeats.	Major	5
7.NS.A.3	Solve real-world and mathematical problems involving the four operations with rational numbers.	Major	8

Expressions and Equations

Use properties of operations to generate equivalent expressions.

7.EE.A.1	Apply properties of operations as strategies to add, subtract, factor, and expand linear expressions with rational coefficients.	Major	14
7.EE.A.2	Understand that rewriting an expression in different forms in a problem context can shed light on the problem and how the quantities in it are related. *For example, a + 0.05a = 1.05a means that "increase by 5%" is the same as "multiply by 1.05."*	Major	15

The Standards for Mathematical Practice are integrated throughout the instructional lessons.

Expressions and Equations *continued*

Solve real-life and mathematical problems using numerical and algebraic expressions and equations.

7.EE.B.3	Solve multi-step real-life and mathematical problems posed with positive and negative rational numbers in any form (whole numbers, fractions, and decimals), using tools strategically. Apply properties of operations to calculate with numbers in any form; convert between forms as appropriate; and assess the reasonableness of answers using mental computation and estimation strategies. *For example: If a woman making $25 an hour gets a 10% raise, she will make an additional $\frac{1}{10}$ of her salary an hour, or $2.50, for a new salary of $27.50. If you want to place a towel bar $9\frac{3}{4}$ inches long in the center of a door that is $27\frac{1}{2}$ inches wide, you will need to place the bar about 9 inches from each edge; this estimate can be used as a check on the exact computation.*	Major	8, 16, 17
7.EE.B.4	Use variables to represent quantities in a real-world or mathematical problem, and construct simple equations and inequalities to solve problems by reasoning about the quantities.	Major	16, 17
7.EE.B.4a	Solve word problems leading to equations of the form $px + q = r$ and $p(x + q) = r$, where p, q, and r are specific rational numbers. Solve equations of these forms fluently. Compare an algebraic solution to an arithmetic solution, identifying the sequence of the operations used in each approach. *For example, the perimeter of a rectangle is 54 cm. Its length is 6 cm. What is its width?*	Major	16
7.EE.B.4b	Solve word problems leading to inequalities of the form $px + q > r$ or $px + q , r$, where $p, q,$ and r are specific rational numbers. Graph the solution set of the inequality and interpret it in the context of the problem. *For example: As a salesperson, you are paid $50 per week plus $3 per sale. This week you want your pay to be at least $100. Write an inequality for the number of sales you need to make, and describe the solutions.*	Major	17

Geometry

Draw, construct, and describe geometrical figures and describe the relationships between them.

7.G.A.1	Solve problems involving scale drawings of geometric figures, such as computing actual lengths and areas from a scale drawing and reproducing a scale drawing at a different scale.	Supporting/ Additional	22
7.G.A.2	Draw (freehand, with ruler and protractor, and with technology) geometric shapes with given conditions. Focus on constructing triangles from three measures of angles or sides, noticing when the conditions determine a unique triangle, more than one triangle, or no triangle.	Supporting/ Additional	19
7.G.A.3	Describe the two-dimensional figures that result from slicing three-dimensional figures, as in plane sections of right rectangular prisms and right rectangular pyramids.	Supporting/ Additional	25

The Standards for Mathematical Practice are integrated throughout the instructional lessons.

Geometry *continued*

Solve real-life and mathematical problems involving angle measure, area, surface area, and volume.

		Content Emphasis	Ready® Lesson(s)
7.G.B.4	Know the formulas for the area and circumference of a circle and use them to solve problems; give an informal derivation of the relationship between the circumference and area of a circle.	Supporting/ Additional	21
7.G.B.5	Use facts about supplementary, complementary, vertical, and adjacent angles in a multi-step problem to write and solve simple equations for an unknown angle in a figure.	Supporting/ Additional	18
7.G.B.6	Solve real-world and mathematical problems involving area, volume and surface area of two- and three-dimensional objects composed of triangles, quadrilaterals, polygons, cubes, and right prisms.	Supporting/ Additional	20, 23, 24

Statistics and Probability

Use random sampling to draw inferences about a population.

		Content Emphasis	Ready® Lesson(s)
7.SP.A.1	Understand that statistics can be used to gain information about a population by examining a sample of the population; generalizations about a population from a sample are valid only if the sample is representative of that population. Understand that random sampling tends to produce representative samples and support valid inferences.	Supporting/ Additional	26
7.SP.A.2	Use data from a random sample to draw inferences about a population with an unknown characteristic of interest. Generate multiple samples (or simulated samples) of the same size to gauge the variation in estimates or predictions. *For example, estimate the mean word length in a book by randomly sampling words from the book; predict the winner of a school election based on randomly sampled survey data. Gauge how far off the estimate or prediction might be.*	Supporting/ Additional	27

Draw informal and comparative inferences about two populations.

		Content Emphasis	Ready® Lesson(s)
7.SP.B.3	Informally assess the degree of visual overlap of two numerical data distributions with similar variabilities, measuring the difference between the centers by expressing it as a multiple of a measure of variability. *For example, the mean height of players on the basketball team is 10 cm greater than the mean height of players on the soccer team, about twice the variability (mean absolute deviation) on either team; on a dot plot, the separation between the two distributions of heights is noticeable.*	Supporting/ Additional	28
7.SP.B.4	Use measures of center and measures of variability for numerical data from random samples to draw informal comparative inferences about two populations. *For example, decide whether the words in a chapter of a seventh-grade science book are generally longer than the words in a chapter of a fourth-grade science book.*	Supporting/ Additional	29

The Standards for Mathematical Practice are integrated throughout the instructional lessons.

Common Core State Standards for Grade 7 Mathematical Standards	Content Emphasis	Ready® Lesson(s)
Statistics and Probability *continued*		
Investigate chance processes and develop, use, and evaluate probability models.		
7.SP.C.5 Understand that the probability of a chance event is a number between 0 and 1 that expresses the likelihood of the event occurring. Larger numbers indicate greater likelihood. A probability near 0 indicates an unlikely event, a probability around $\frac{1}{2}$ indicates an event that is neither unlikely nor likely, and a probability near 1 indicates a likely event.	Supporting/ Additional	30
7.SP.C.6 Approximate the probability of a chance event by collecting data on the chance process that produces it and observing its long-run relative frequency, and predict the approximate relative frequency given the probability. *For example, when rolling a number cube 600 times, predict that a 3 or 6 would be rolled roughly 200 times, but probably not exactly 200 times.*	Supporting/ Additional	31
7.SP.C.7 Understand that attributes belonging to a category of two-dimensional figures also belong to all subcategories of that category. *For example, all rectangles have four right angles and squares are rectangles, so all squares have four right angles.*	Supporting/ Additional	32
7.SP.C.7a Develop a uniform probability model by assigning equal probability to all outcomes, and use the model to determine probabilities of events. *For example, if a student is selected at random from a class, find the probability that Jane will be selected and the probability that a girl will be selected.*	Supporting/ Additional	32
7.SP.C.7b Develop a probability model (which may not be uniform) by observing frequencies in data generated from a chance process. *For example, find the approximate probability that a spinning penny will land heads up or that a tossed paper cup will land open-end down. Do the outcomes for the spinning penny appear to be equally likely based on the observed frequencies?*	Supporting/ Additional	32
7.SP.C.8 Find probabilities of compound events using organized lists, tables, tree diagrams, and simulation.	Supporting/ Additional	33
7.SP.C.8a Understand that, just as with simple events, the probability of a compound event is the fraction of outcomes in the sample space for which the compound event occurs.	Supporting/ Additional	33
7.SP.C.8b Represent sample spaces for compound events using methods such as organized lists, tables and tree diagrams. *For an event described in everyday language (e.g., "rolling double sixes"), identify the outcomes in the sample space which compose the event.*	Supporting/ Additional	33
7.SP.C.8c Design and use a simulation to generate frequencies for compound events. *For example, use random digits as a simulation tool to approximate the answer to the question: If 40% of donors have type A blood, what is the probability that it will take at least 4 donors to find one with type A blood?*	Supporting/ Additional	33

The Standards for Mathematical Practice are integrated throughout the instructional lessons.

Acknowledgments

Illustration Credits

page 183: Sam Valentino (wooden gate)

page 214: daulon/Shutterstock/DES (great white shark)

page 215: Shutterstock (model car)

page 217: Michele Paccione/Shutterstock (plants)

page 226: Sam Valentino (bird house)

page 248: Sam Valentino (jar of folded paper names)

page 280: dgbomb/Shutterstock (number cube)

Background images used throughout lessons by Ortis/Shutterstock, irin-k/Shutterstock, and Kritsada Namborisut/Shutterstock.